ANALYTIC GEOMETRY

ADDISON–WESLEY MATHEMATICS SERIES

ERIC REISSNER, *Consulting Editor*

Bardell and Spitzbart—COLLEGE ALGEBRA

Dadourian—PLANE TRIGONOMETRY

Davis—MODERN COLLEGE GEOMETRY

Davis—THE TEACHING OF MATHEMATICS

Fuller—ANALYTIC GEOMETRY

Gnedenko and Kolmogorov—LIMIT DISTRIBUTIONS FOR SUMS OF INDEPENDENT RANDOM VARIABLES

Kaplan—ADVANCED CALCULUS

Kaplan—A FIRST COURSE IN FUNCTIONS OF A COMPLEX VARIABLE

Meserve—FUNDAMENTAL CONCEPTS OF ALGEBRA

Munroe—INTRODUCTION TO MEASURE AND INTEGRATION

Perlis—THEORY OF MATRICES

Stabler—AN INTRODUCTION TO MATHEMATICAL THOUGHT

Struik—DIFFERENTIAL GEOMETRY

Struik—ELEMENTARY ANALYTIC AND PROJECTIVE GEOMETRY

Thomas—CALCULUS

Thomas—CALCULUS AND ANALYTIC GEOMETRY

Wade—THE ALGEBRA OF VECTORS AND MATRICES

Wilkes, Wheeler, and Gill—THE PREPARATION OF PROGRAMS FOR AN ELECTRONIC DIGITAL COMPUTER

ANALYTIC GEOMETRY

by

GORDON FULLER

Professor of Mathematics
Texas Technological College

1954

ADDISON–WESLEY PUBLISHING COMPANY, Inc.

CAMBRIDGE 42, MASS.

516
F 965

NOV 2 1955

3.99

PREFACE

In recent years there has been a marked tendency in college mathematics programs toward an earlier and more intensive use of the methods of calculus. This change is made in response to the fact that college students are faced with more and more applications of mathematics in engineering, physics, chemistry, and other fields. There is a pressing need for a working knowledge of calculus as early as possible. Consequently many teachers are making a close scrutiny of the traditional topics of freshman mathematics. This is done in an effort to determine the material and emphasis which will lay the best foundation for the study of calculus.

In the light of present needs, this analytic geometry is planned primarily as a preparation for calculus. With this end in mind, a few of the usual topics are not included and certain others are treated with brevity. The omitted material, consisting of an appreciable amount of the geometry of circles and a number of minor items, is not essential to the study of calculus. The time saved by cutting traditional material provides opportunity for emphasizing the necessary basic principles and for introducing new concepts which point more directly toward the calculus.

Students come to analytic geometry with a rather limited experience in graphing. Principally they have dealt with the graphs of linear and certain quadratic equations. Hence it seems well to let this be the starting point. Accordingly, the first chapter deals with functions and graphs. In order that this part shall go beyond a review of old material, the ideas of intercepts, symmetry, excluded values, and asymptotes are considered.

Most students in algebra are told (without proof) that the graph of a linear equation in two variables is a straight line. Taking cognizance of this situation, it appears logical to prove directly from the equation that the graph of $Ax + By + C = 0$ is a straight line. Having established this fact, the equation can be altered in a straightforward procedure to yield various special forms. The normal form, however, receives only incidental mention.

The transformation of coordinates concept is introduced preceding a systematic study of conics. Taken early or late in the course, this is a difficult idea for the students. By its early use, however, the students may see that a general second degree equation can be reduced to a simple form. Thus there is established a logical basis for investigating conics by means of the simple equations.

Although employing simple forms, the second degree equation is introduced at variance with the traditional procedure. As with the linear equation, it seems logical to build on the previous instruction given to the students. In algebra they have drawn graphs of conics. The words *circle, parabola, ellipse,* and *hyperbola* are familiar to many of them. In fact, some students can classify the type of conic if the equation has no xy term. Tying in with this state of preparation, the conic may naturally and logically be defined analytically rather than as the locus of a moving point. The equations then lend themselves to the establishment of various geometric properties.

In harmony with the idea of laying a foundation for calculus, a chapter is given to the use of the derivatives of polynomials and of negative integral powers of a variable. Applications are made in constructing graphs, and some maxima and minima problems of a practical nature are considered.

The chapter on curve fitting applies the method of least squares in fitting a straight line to empirical data.

Many students come to calculus with little understanding of polar coordinates, therefore polar coordinates are discussed quite fully, and there is an abundance of problems.

The elements of solid analytic geometry are treated in two concluding chapters. The first of these takes up quadric surfaces and the second deals with planes and lines. This order is chosen because a class which takes only one of the two chapters should preferably study the space illustrations of second degree equations. Vectors are introduced and applied in the study of planes and lines. This study is facilitated, of course, by the use of vectors, and a further advantage is gained by giving the students a brief encounter with this valuable concept.

The six numerical tables provided in the Appendix, though brief, are fully adequate to meet the needs which arise in the problems.

Answers to odd-numbered problems are bound in the book. All of the answers are available in pamphlet form to teachers.

The book is written for a course of three semester hours. While an exceptionally well prepared group of students will be able to cover the entire book in a course of this length, there will be excess material for many classes. It is suggested that omissions may be made from Chapters 7 and 8, Sections 6–7, 9–8, 12–7, and 12–8.

The author is indebted to Professor B. H. Gere, Hamilton College, Professor Morris Kline, New York University, and Professor Eric Reissner, Massachusetts Institute of Technology. Each of these men read the manuscript at various stages of its development and made numerous helpful suggestions for improvement.

G. F.

January, 1954

CONTENTS

CONTENTS

CHAPTER 1

FUNCTIONS AND GRAPHS

1–1 Introduction. Previous to the seventeenth century, algebra and geometry were largely distinct mathematical sciences, each having been developed independently of the other. In 1637, however, a French mathematician and philosopher, René Descartes, published his *La Géométrie*, which introduced a device for unifying these two branches of mathematics. The basic feature of this new process, now called *analytic geometry*, is the use of a coordinate system. By means of coordinate systems algebraic methods can be applied powerfully in the study of geometry, and perhaps of still greater importance is the advantage gained by algebra through the pictorial representation of algebraic equations. Since the time of Descartes analytic geometry has had a tremendous impact on the development of mathematical knowledge. And today analytic methods enter vitally into the diverse theoretical and practical applications of mathematics.

1–2 Rectangular coordinates. We shall describe the rectangular coordinate system which the student has previously met in elementary algebra and trigonometry. This is the most common coordinate system and is sometimes called the rectangular Cartesian system in honor of Descartes.

Draw two perpendicular lines meeting at O (Fig. 1–1). The point O is called the *origin* and the lines are called the *axes*, OX the x-axis and OY the y-axis. The x-axis is usually drawn horizontally and is frequently referred to as the *horizontal* axis, and the y-axis is called the *vertical* axis. The axes divide their plane into four parts called *quadrants*. The quadrants are numbered I, II, III, and IV, as in Fig. 1–1. Next select any convenient unit of length and lay off distances from the origin along the axes. The distances to the right along the x-axis are defined as *positive* and those to the left are taken as *negative*. Similarly, distances upward along the y-axis are defined as positive and those downward are called negative.

The position of any point P in the plane may be definitely indicated by giving its distances from the axes. The distance from the y-axis to P is called the *abscissa* of the point, and the distance from the x-axis is called the *ordinate* of the point. The abscissa is positive if the point is to the right of the y-axis, and negative if the point is to the left of the y-axis. The ordinate is positive if the point is above the x-axis, and negative if the point is below the x-axis. The abscissa of a point on the y-axis is zero and the ordinate of a point on the x-axis is zero. The two distances,

1

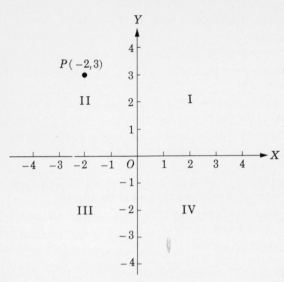

FIGURE 1–1

abscissa and ordinate, are called the *coordinates* of the point. The coordinates are indicated by writing the abscissa first and enclosing both numbers by parentheses. For example, $P(-2,3)$, or just $(-2,3)$, stands for the point whose abscissa is -2 and whose ordinate is 3.

To *plot* a point of given coordinates means to measure the proper distances from the axes and to mark the point thus determined. Points can be more readily and accurately plotted by the use of coordinate paper, that is, paper ruled off into small squares. It is easy to plot a point whose coordinates are distances from the axes to an intersection of two rulings. For other coordinate values the point is not at a corner of one of the small squares and its position within or on the side of the square must be estimated. If a coordinate is an irrational number, a decimal approximation is used in plotting the point.

We assume that to any pair of real numbers (coordinates) there corresponds one definite point of the coordinate plane. Conversely, we assume that to each point of the plane there corresponds one definite pair of coordinates. This relation of points in a plane and pairs of real numbers is called a *one-to-one correspondence*.

EXERCISE 1–1

1. Plot the points whose coordinates are $(4,3)$, $(4,-3)$, $(-4,3)$, $(-4,-3)$, $(5,0)$, $(0,-2)$, and $(0,0)$.

2. Plot the points whose coordinates are $(\frac{1}{2},\frac{3}{4})$, $(\frac{3}{5},\frac{5}{2})$, $(\frac{11}{3},-4)$, $(\frac{21}{4},\frac{7}{5})$, $(\sqrt{2},1)$, $(\sqrt{3},\sqrt{3})$, $(\sqrt{5},-\sqrt{10})$. (See Table I in the Appendix to obtain square roots.)

3. Draw the triangles whose vertices are (a) $(2,-1)$, $(0,4)$, $(5,1)$; (b) $(2,-3)$, $(4,4)$, $(-2,3)$.

4. In which quadrant does a point lie if (a) both coordinates are positive, (b) both are negative?

5. Where may a point lie if (a) its ordinate is zero, (b) its abscissa is zero?

6. What points have their abscissas equal to 2? For what points are the ordinates equal to -2?

7. Where may a point be if (a) its abscissa is equal to its ordinate, (b) its abscissa is equal to the negative of its ordinate?

8. Draw the right triangle and find the lengths of the sides and hypotenuse if the coordinates of the vertices are (a) $(-1,1)$, $(3,1)$, $(3,-2)$; (b) $(-5,3)$, $(7,3)$, $(7,-2)$.

9. Two vertices of an equilateral triangle are $(3,0)$ and $(-3,0)$. Find the coordinates of the third vertex and the area of the triangle.

10. The points $A(0,0)$, $B(5,1)$, and $C(1,3)$ are vertices of a parallelogram. Find the coordinates of the fourth vertex (a) if BC is a diagonal, (b) if AB is a diagonal, (c) if AC is a diagonal.

1–3 Variables and functions. Numbers, and letters standing for numbers, are used in mathematics. The numbers, of course, are fixed in value. A letter may stand for a fixed number which is unknown or unspecified. The numbers and letters standing for fixed quantities are called *constants*. Letters are also used as symbols which may assume different numerical values. When employed for this purpose, the letter is said to be a *variable*.

For example, we may use the formula $c = 2\pi r$ to find the circumference of any circle of known radius. The letters c and r are variables; they play a different role from the fixed numbers 2 and π. A quadratic expression in *the variable x* may be represented by

$$ax^2 + bx + c,$$

where we regard a, b, and c as unspecified constants which assume fixed values in a particular problem or situation.

Variable quantities are often related in such a way that one variable depends on another for its values. The relationship of variables is a basic concept in mathematics, and we shall be concerned with this idea throughout the book.

DEFINITION. *If a definite value or set of values of a variable y is determined when a variable x takes any one of its values, then y is said to be a function of x.*

Frequently the relation between two variables is expressed by an equation. The equation $c = 2\pi r$ expresses the relation between the circumference and radius of a circle. When any positive value is assigned to r, the value of c is determined. Hence c is a function of r. The radius is also a function of the circumference, since r is determined when c is given a value.

Usually we assign values to one variable and find the corresponding values of the other. The variable to which we assign values is called the *independent variable*, and the other, the *dependent variable*.

The equation $x^2 - y + 2 = 0$ expresses a relation between the variables x and y. Either may be regarded as the independent variable. Solving for y, the equation becomes $y = x^2 + 2$. In this form we consider x the independent variable. When expressed in the form $x = \pm\sqrt{y - 2}$, we consider y the independent variable. We notice from the equation $y = x^2 + 2$ that y takes only one value for each value given to x. The variable y therefore is said to be a *single-valued* function of x. On the other hand, taking y as the independent variable, we see that for each value given to y there are two corresponding values of x. Hence x is a *double-valued* function of y.

Restrictions are usually placed on the values which a variable may take. We shall consider variables which have only real values. This requirement means that the independent variable can be assigned only those real values for which the corresponding values of the dependent variable are also real. The totality of values which a variable may take is called the *range* of the variable. In the equation $c = 2\pi r$, giving the circumference of a circle as a function of the radius, r and c take only positive values. Hence the range for each variable consists of all positive numbers. The equation

$$y = \frac{\sqrt{9 - x^2}}{x - 2}$$

expresses y as a function of x. The permissible values of x are those from -3 to 3 with the exception of 2. The value 2 would make the denominator zero, and must be excluded because division by zero is not defined. This range of x may be written symbolically as

$$-3 \leq x < 2, \quad 2 < x \leq 3.$$

1–4 Useful notation for functions. Suppose that $y = x^2 - 3x + 5$. To indicate that y is a function of x, we write the symbol $y(x)$. Using this notation, the equation is written as

$$y(x) = x^2 - 3x + 5.$$

The symbol $y(x)$ is read y *function of* x, or, more simply, y *of* x. In a problem where there are different functions of x we could designate them by different letters such as $f(x)$, $g(x)$, and $h(x)$. Letters other than x, of course, could stand for the independent variable.

If $y(x)$ stands for a function of x, then $y(2)$ means the value of the function, or y, when x is given the value of 2. Thus if

$$y(x) = x^2 - 3x + 5,$$

then

$$y(2) = 2^2 - 3(2) + 5 = 3,$$
$$y(-1) = (-1)^2 - 3(-1) + 5 = 9,$$
$$y(s) = s^2 - 3s + 5.$$

EXERCISE 1–2

1. Give the range of x, if x and y are to have only real values:

    (a) $y = \dfrac{1}{(x-2)(x+3)}$;   (b) $y = \sqrt{x(1-x)}$;   (c) $y = \dfrac{\sqrt{x-3}}{x-4}$.

Solve the equations in problems 2 and 3 for each variable in terms of the other. Give the range of each variable and tell if each is a single-valued or double-valued function of the other.

2. (a) $x^2 + y^2 = 9$; (b) $x^2 + 2y^2 = 2$; (c) $y^2 = x^3$.

3. (a) $y^2 = 4x$; (b) $xy = 5$; (c) $x^2 - y^2 = 9$.

4. If $f(x) = x^2 - 3$, find $f(2)$, $f(-3)$, and $f(a)$.

5. If $g(x) = x^3 - x^2 + 1$, find $g(0)$, $g(-1)$, and $g(s)$.

6. If $f(x) = x^3 - 1$ and $g(x) = x - 1$, find $f(x) \div g(x)$.

7. If $h(s) = 2s + 3$, find $h(2t)$, $h(t + 1)$, and $h(t^2)$.

8. If $y(x) = 2x^2 - 3x + 1$, find $y(x - 1)$.

9. If $F(x) = \dfrac{x-1}{x+1}$, find $F(2x)$, $F(x - 3)$, and $F\left(\dfrac{1}{x}\right)$.

10. If $f(x) = 3x^4 + 2x^2 - 10$, show that $f(-x) = f(x)$.

1–5 Graph of an equation. Consider the equation

$$y = x^2 - 3x - 3.$$

If values are assigned to x, the corresponding values of y may be computed. Thus, setting $x = -2$, we find $y = 7$. Several values of x and the corresponding values of y are shown in the table. These pairs of values furnish a picture of the relation of x and y. A better representation is had, however, by plotting each value of x and the corresponding value of y as the abscissa and ordinate of a point, and then drawing a smooth curve through the points thus obtained. This process is called *graphing the equation*, and the curve is called the *graph* or *locus* of the equation.

x	-2	-1	0	1	1.5	2	3	4	5
y	7	1	-3	-5	-5.25	-5	-3	1	7

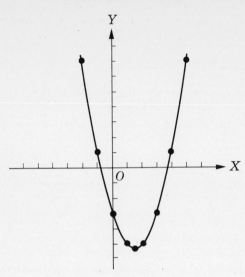

FIGURE 1–2

The plotted points (Fig. 1–2) are in the range −2 to 5 of x-values. The range could be extended, and also any number of intermediate points could be located. But the points plotted show about where the intermediate points would lie. Hence, we can use the known points to draw a curve which is reasonably accurate. The exact graph satisfies the following definition.

DEFINITION. *The graph of an equation consists of all the points whose coordinates satisfy the given equation.*

1–6 Aids in graphing. The point-by-point method of constructing the graph of an equation is tedious except for simple equations. The task can often be lightened, however, by first discovering certain characteristics of the graph as revealed by the equation. We shall now discuss three ways by which the graphing may be facilitated.

Intercepts. The abscissa of a point where a curve touches or crosses the x-axis is called an *x-intercept*. The ordinate of a point where a curve touches or crosses the y-axis is called a *y-intercept*. To find the x-intercepts of the graph of an equation, we set $y = 0$ and solve for x. Similarly, the y-intercepts may be found by setting $x = 0$ and solving for y. Thus setting $y = 0$ in the equation $2x - 3y = 6$, we find $x = 3$. The point $(3,0)$ is on the graph and the x-intercept is 3. Substituting $x = 0$, the y-intercept is found to be -2.

The graphs of some equations have no points in common with an axis;

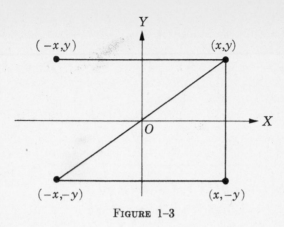

FIGURE 1–3

for other equations there may be few or many intercepts. The intercepts are often easily determined, and are of special significance in many problems.

SYMMETRY. *Two points A and B are said to be symmetric with respect to a line if the line is the perpendicular bisector of the segment AB. A curve is symmetric with respect to a line if each of its points is one of a pair of points symmetric with respect to the line.*

At present our interest is mainly in curves which are symmetric with respect to the coordinate axes. The points (x,y) and $(x,-y)$ are symmetric with respect to the x-axis. A curve is symmetric with respect to the x-axis if for each point (x,y) of the curve there is also the point $(x,-y)$ on the curve. Similarly, a curve is symmetric with respect to the y-axis if for each point (x,y) of the curve there is also the point $(-x,y)$ on the curve. (See Fig. 1–3.)

Two points A and B are symmetric with respect to a point O if O is the mid-point of the line segment AB. A curve is symmetric with respect to a point O if each point of the curve is one of a pair of points symmetric with respect to O.

In accordance with this definition, the points (x,y) and $(-x,-y)$ are symmetric with respect to the origin. Further, a curve is symmetric with respect to the origin if for each point (x,y) of the curve there is also the corresponding point $(-x,-y)$ on the curve.

An equation can be easily tested to determine if its graph is symmetric with respect to either axis or the origin. Consider, for example, the equation $y^2 = 4x + 6$. If y is replaced by $-y$, the equation is not altered. This means that if y is given a value and then the negative of that value, the corresponding values of x are the same. Hence for each point (x,y)

of the graph there is also the point $(x, -y)$ on the graph. The graph therefore is symmetric with respect to the x-axis. On the other hand, the assigning of numerically equal values of opposite signs to x leads to different corresponding values for y. Hence the graph is not symmetric with respect to the y-axis. Similarly, it may be observed that the graph is not symmetric with respect to the origin.

From the definitions of symmetry we have the following tests.

1. *If an equation is unchanged when y is replaced by $-y$, then the graph of the equation is symmetric with respect to the x-axis.*

2. *If an equation is unchanged when x is replaced by $-x$, then the graph of the equation is symmetric with respect to the y-axis.*

3. *If an equation is unchanged when x is replaced by $-x$ and y by $-y$, then the graph of the equation is symmetric with respect to the origin.*

These types of symmetry are illustrated by the equations

$$y^4 - 2y^2 - x = 0, \quad x^2 - 4y + 3 = 0, \quad y = x^3.$$

The graphs of these equations are respectively symmetric with respect to the x-axis, the y-axis, and the origin. Replacing x by $-x$ and y by $-y$ in the third equation gives $-y = -x^3$, which may be reduced to $y = x^3$.

Extent of a graph. Only real values of x and y are used in graphing an equation. Hence no value may be assigned to either which would make the corresponding value of the other imaginary. Some equations may have any real value assigned to either variable. On the other hand, an equation by its nature may place restrictions on the values of the variables. Where there are certain excluded values, the graph of the equation is correspondingly restricted in its extent. Frequently the admissible, and therefore the excluded, values are readily determined by solving the equation for each variable in terms of the other.

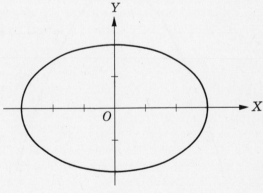

FIGURE 1-4

EXAMPLE 1.   Using the ideas of intercepts, symmetry, and extent, discuss the equation $4x^2 + 9y^2 = 36$, and draw its graph.

Solution.   Setting $y = 0$, we find $x = \pm 3$. Hence the x-intercepts are -3 and 3.   By setting $x = 0$, the y-intercepts are seen to be -2 and 2.

The equation is not changed when x is replaced by $-x$; neither is it changed when y is replaced by $-y$.   The graph therefore is symmetric with respect to both axes and the origin.

Solving the equation for each variable in terms of the other, we obtain

$$y = \pm \tfrac{2}{3}\sqrt{9 - x^2} \qquad \text{and} \qquad x = \pm \tfrac{3}{2}\sqrt{4 - y^2}.$$

If $9 - x^2$ is negative, y is imaginary.   Hence x cannot have a value numerically greater than 3.   In other words, x takes values from -3 to 3, which is expressed symbolically by $-3 \le x \le 3$.   Similarly, values of y numerically greater than 2 must be excluded.   Hence the admissible values for y are $-2 \le y \le 2$.

A brief table of values, coupled with the preceding information, is sufficient for constructing the graph.   The part of the graph in the first quadrant (Fig. 1–4) comes from the table; the other is drawn in accordance with the known symmetry.

x	0	1	2	3
y	2	$\tfrac{2}{3}\sqrt{8} = 1.9$	$\tfrac{2}{3}\sqrt{5} = 1.5$	0

EXAMPLE 2.   Graph the equation $x^2 + 4y - 12 = 0$.

Solution.   Setting $y = 0$ and then $x = 0$, we find the x-intercepts $= \pm 2\sqrt{3}$ and the y-intercept $= 3$.

If x is replaced by $-x$, the equation is unchanged.   A new equation results when y is replaced by $-y$.   Hence the graph is symmetric with respect to the y-axis, but not with respect to the x-axis or the origin.

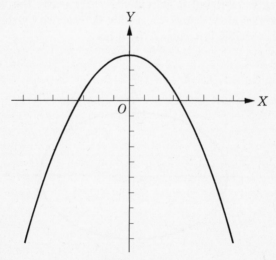

FIGURE 1–5

Solving the equation in turn for x and y, we obtain

$$x = \pm 2\sqrt{3 - y} \qquad \text{and} \qquad y = \frac{12 - x^2}{4}.$$

We see that y must not be greater than 3, but x has no excluded values.

From the preceding facts and the table of values the graph is drawn in Fig. 1–5. Only a part of the graph is indicated because the curve extends downward indefinitely.

x	0	1	2	3.46	4	5	6
y	3	2.75	2	0	-1	-3.25	-6

EXERCISE 1–3

Discuss each equation with regard to intercepts and symmetry. Determine the excluded values, if any, of each variable, and draw the graph. (See Table I in the Appendix to obtain square roots.)

1. $x^2 + y^2 = 16$.

2. $y^2 = 9x$.

3. $x^2 = y - 4$.

4. $x^2 - y^2 = 16$.

5. $9x^2 + 4y^2 = 36$.

6. $4x^2 - 9y^2 = 36$.

7. $y = x^3$.

8. $y = x^3 - 4x$.

9. $y^2 = x^3$.

10. $y^2 = x^3 - 4x$.

11. $9y^2 - 16x^2 = 144$.

12. $25x^2 + 9y^2 = 225$.

13. Prove that a curve which is symmetric with respect to both axes is symmetric with respect to the origin. Is the converse true?

14. Prove that a curve which is symmetric with respect to the x-axis and the origin is symmetric with respect to the y-axis.

1–7 The graph of an equation in factored form. Equations sometimes appear with one member equal to zero and the other member expressed as the product of factors in terms of x and y. When an equation is in this form its graph can be more simply obtained by first setting each of the factors equal to zero. If the coordinates of a point make one of the factors equal to zero, they make the product equal to zero and therefore satisfy the given equation. On the other hand, the coordinates of a point which make no factor equal to zero do not satisfy the equation. Hence the graph of the given equation consists of the graphs of the equations formed by setting each of the factors of the nonzero member equal to zero.

EXAMPLE. Draw the graph of $(3x - y - 1)(y^2 - 9x) = 0$.

Solution. Setting each factor equal to zero, we have the equations

$$3x - y - 1 = 0 \qquad \text{and} \qquad y^2 - 9x = 0.$$

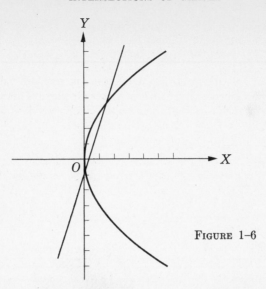

FIGURE 1–6

The equation $3x - y - 1 = 0$ is of the first degree in x and y. We shall see later that the graph of any first degree equation in two variables is a straight line. For this reason such equations are called *linear*. Hence the graph of a linear equation can be constructed by drawing a line through two points whose coordinates satisfy the equation. The second equation is not linear, and several points need to be plotted in order to draw the graph. The graph of the original equation comprises the two parts shown in Fig. 1–6.

EXERCISE 1–4

Draw the graphs of the following equations:

1. $x^2 - y^2 = 0$.
2. $(x + 1)(2x + y + 4) = 0$.
3. $(x - 2y + 3)(2x + y + 4) = 0$.
4. $xy(x + y - 2) = 0$.
5. $x^2 - xy - 6y^2 = 0$.
6. $y^2 - xy - 4y = 0$.
7. $x^2y - 9y^2 = 0$.
8. $x(x^2 + y^2 - 4) = 0$.
9. $\dfrac{x^2}{9} - \dfrac{y^2}{16} = 0$.
10. $\dfrac{y^2}{4} - \dfrac{x^2}{25} = 0$.

1–8 Intersections of graphs. If the graphs of two equations in two variables have a point in common, then, from the definition of a graph, the coordinates of the point satisfy each equation separately. Hence the point of intersection gives a pair of real numbers which is a simultaneous solution of the equations. Conversely, if the two equations have a simultaneous real solution, then their graphs have the corresponding point in common. Hence simultaneous real solutions of two equations in two unknowns can be obtained graphically by reading the coordinates of their points of intersection. Because of the imperfections in the process, the results thus found are usually only approximate. If the graphs have no point of intersection, there is no real solution.   In simple cases the solutions, both real and imaginary, can be found exactly by algebraic processes.

EXAMPLE 1.   Draw the graphs of the equations

$$y^2 - 9x = 0,$$
$$3x - y - 1 = 0,$$

and estimate the coordinates of the points of intersection.   Solve the system algebraically and compare results.

Solution.   These are the equations whose graphs are shown in Fig. 1–6.   Referring to this figure, we estimate the coordinates of the intersection points to be $(.1, -.8)$ and $(1.6, 3.8)$.

To obtain the solutions algebraically, we solve the linear equation for x and substitute in the other equation.   Thus

$$x = \frac{y + 1}{3} \quad \text{and} \quad y^2 - 9\left(\frac{y + 1}{3}\right) = 0,$$

whence

$$y^2 - 3y - 3 = 0, \quad \text{and} \quad y = \frac{3 \pm \sqrt{21}}{2}.$$

By substituting these values in the linear equation, the corresponding values for x are found to be $(5 \pm \sqrt{21})/6$.   Hence the exact coordinates of the intersection points are

$$\left(\frac{5 + \sqrt{21}}{6}, \frac{3 + \sqrt{21}}{2}\right) \quad \text{and} \quad \left(\frac{5 - \sqrt{21}}{6}, \frac{3 - \sqrt{21}}{2}\right).$$

These coordinates to two decimal places are $(1.60, 3.79)$ and $(.07, -.79)$.

EXAMPLE 2.   Find the points of intersection of the graphs of

$$y = x^3, \quad y = 2 - x.$$

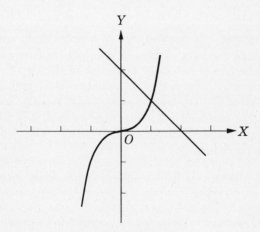

FIGURE 1–7

Solution. The graphs (Fig. 1–7) intersect in one point whose coordinates are (1,1).

Eliminating y between the equations yields

$$x^3 + x - 2 = 0, \quad \text{or} \quad (x - 1)(x^2 + x + 2) = 0,$$

whence

$$x = 1, \quad \frac{-1 + \sqrt{-7}}{2}, \quad \frac{-1 - \sqrt{-7}}{2}.$$

The corresponding values of y are obtained from the linear equation. The solutions, real and imaginary, are

$$(1,1); \quad \left(\frac{-1 + \sqrt{-7}}{2}, \frac{5 - \sqrt{-7}}{2}\right); \quad \left(\frac{-1 - \sqrt{-7}}{2}, \frac{5 + \sqrt{-7}}{2}\right).$$

The graphical method gives only the real solution.

EXERCISE 1–5

Graph each pair of equations and estimate the coordinates of any points of intersection. Check by obtaining the solutions algebraically.

1. $x + 2y = 7,$
   $3x - 2y = 5.$

2. $2x - y = 3,$
   $5x + 3y = 8.$

3. $x^2 + y^2 = 13,$
   $3x - 2y = 0.$

4. $x^2 - 4y = 0,$
   $y^2 = 6x.$

5. $x^2 + 2y^2 = 9,$
   $2x - y = 0.$

6. $x^2 + y^2 = 16,$
   $y^2 = 6x.$

7. $y = x^3,$
   $y = 4x.$

8. $y = x^2,$
   $x + y - 1 = 0.$

9. $x^2 - y^2 = 9,$
   $x^2 + y^2 = 16.$

10. $y = x^3 - 4x,$
    $y = x + 4.$

11. $y^2 = 8x,$
    $2x - y = 4.$

12. $x^2 + 4y^2 = 25,$
    $4x^2 - 7y^2 = 8.$

1–9 Asymptotes. If the distance of a point from a straight line approaches zero as the point moves indefinitely far from the origin along a curve, then the line is called an *asymptote* of the curve. (See Figs. 1–8, 1–9.) In drawing the graph of an equation it is well to determine the asymptotes, if any. The asymptotes, usually easily found, furnish an additional aid in graphing. At this stage we shall deal with curves whose asymptotes are either horizontal or vertical. The following examples illustrate the procedure.

EXAMPLE 1. Determine the asymptotes and draw the graph of the equation

$$xy = 1.$$

Solution. The graph is symmetric with respect to the origin. We next notice that if either variable is set equal to zero, there is no corresponding value of the other variable which satisfies the equation. This means that there is no intercept on either axis, and also that zero is an excluded value for both variables. There are no other excluded values, however.

Solving for y, the equation takes the form

$$y = \frac{1}{x}.$$

Suppose we give to x successively the values 1, $\frac{1}{2}$, $\frac{1}{4}$, $\frac{1}{8}$, $\frac{1}{16}$, and so on. The corresponding values of y are 1, 2, 4, 8, 16, and so on. We see that as x is assigned values nearer and nearer zero, y becomes larger and larger. In fact, by taking x small enough, the corresponding value of y can be made to exceed any chosen number. This relation is described by saying that as x approaches zero, y increases without limit. Hence the curve extends upward indefinitely as the distances from points on the curve to the y-axis approach zero. The y-axis is therefore an asymptote of the curve.

Similarly, if we assign values to x which get large without limit, then y, being the reciprocal of x, approaches zero. Hence the curve extends indefinitely to the right, getting nearer and nearer to the x-axis, yet never touching it. The x-axis is an asymptote of the curve. Since there is symmetry with respect to the origin, the graph consists of the two parts drawn in Fig. 1–8.

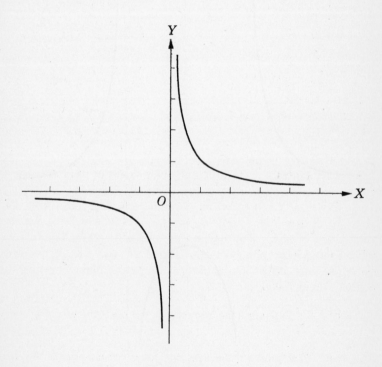

FIGURE 1–8

EXAMPLE 2.   Draw the graph of $x^2y - 4y = 8$.

Solution.   The y-intercept is -2.   But if we set $y = 0$, there is obviously no value of x which will satisfy the equation.   Hence there is no x-intercept.   The graph has symmetry with respect to the y-axis but not with respect to the x-axis. The part of the graph to the right of the y-axis may first be determined and then the other drawn by the use of symmetry.

Solving the equation for y gives

$$y = \frac{8}{x^2 - 4}. \tag{1}$$

Notice the right member of the equation.   We see that it is negative for $-2 < x < 2$, and the graph in this range is below the x-axis.   Further, if x has a value slightly less than 2, the denominator is near zero.   Then the fraction, which is equal to y, has a numerically large value.   As x increases still closer to 2, the corresponding values of y can be made to increase numerically without limit.   If, however, x approaches 2 through values greater than 2, the values of y are positive and increase without limit.   Hence the line $x = 2$ is an asymptote of the curve both below and above the x-axis.

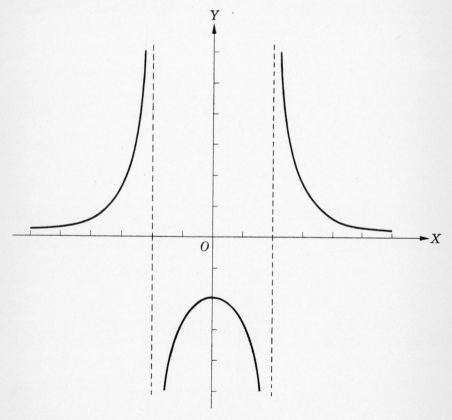

FIGURE 1–9

x	0	1	1.5	1.9	1.99	1.999
y	-2	-2.7	-4.6	-20.5	-200	-2005

To examine for a horizontal asymptote, we notice equation (1) and let x become large without limit. The corresponding values of y approach zero, and $y = 0$ is therefore an asymptote. This asymptote also becomes evident when the given equation is solved for x. Taking the positive roots, we get

$$x = 2\sqrt{\frac{y+2}{y}}.$$

In this form we see that as y approaches zero through positive values, x increases without limit. This shows that $y = 0$ is an asymptote. This form also reveals the excluded values of y. Since the radicand is not to be negative, the values $-2 < y < 0$ are excluded.

The graph is constructed in Fig. 1–9.

In each of the preceding problems the asymptotes are evident when the equation is solved for each variable in terms of the other. For equations which are thus readily solvable, we state the following rules.

1. *Solve the given equation for y in terms of x. If the result is a fraction whose denominator contains x, set each real linear factor of the denominator equal to zero. This gives the vertical asymptotes.*

2. *Solve the given equation for x in terms of y. If the result is a fraction whose denominator contains y, set each real linear factor of the denominator equal to zero. This gives the horizontal asymptotes.*

EXERCISE 1–6

Discuss and sketch the graphs of each of the following equations. Draw the horizontal and vertical asymptotes.

1. $xy + 1 = 0$.
2. $xy - x = 3$.
3. $(x + 1)(y - 1) = 1$.
4. $xy + 3x - 2y - 8 = 0$.
5. $xy^2 = 4$.
6. $x^2y - 9 = 0$.
7. $x^3y = 8$.
8. $x^3y^2 = 64$.
9. $xy^2 + 3y^2 - 4 = 0$.
10. $x^2y + 3x^2 - 4 = 0$.
11. $x^2y - y = 4$.
12. $xy^2 - x - 4 = 0$.
13. $y^2(x + 3) = 10$.
14. $x^2y - x^2 + 4y + 4 = 0$.
15. $y(x - 2)^2 = 16$.
16. $xy^2 + y^2 + 4x + 4 = 0$.
17. $x^2y + 9y = 4$.
18. $x^2y^2 + 9y^2 = 4$.
19. $x^2y^2 - x^2 - 4y^2 = 0$.
20. $x^2y^2 - x^2 + 4y^2 = 0$.
21. $x^2y - x^2 - 9y + 16 = 0$.
22. $x^2y - x^2 - 16y + 9 = 0$.
23. $x^2y^2 - x^2 - 9y^2 + 16 = 0$.
24. $x^2y^2 - x^2 - 16y^2 + 9 = 0$.

CHAPTER 2

FUNDAMENTAL CONCEPTS AND FORMULAS

2–1 Directed lines and segments. A line on which one direction is defined as positive and the opposite direction as negative is called a *directed line*. In analytic geometry important use is made of directed lines. Either direction along a given line may be chosen as positive. The x-axis and lines parallel to it are positive to the right. Vertical lines have their positive direction chosen upward. A line not parallel to a coordinate axis, when regarded as directed, may have either direction taken as positive.

The part of a line between two of its points is called a *segment*. In plane geometry the lengths of line segments are considered, but directions are not assigned to the segments. In analytic geometry, however, line segments are often considered as having directions as well as lengths. Thus in Fig. 2–1, AB means the segment from A to B, and BA stands for the segment from B to A. The segment AB is positive, since the direction from A to B agrees with the assigned positive direction of the line as indicated by the arrowhead. The segment BA, on the other hand, is negative. If there are 3 units of length between A and B, for example, then $AB = +3$ and $BA = -3$. Hence, in referring to directed segments,

$$AB = -BA.$$

If A, B, and C are three points of a directed line, then the directed segments determined by these points satisfy the equations

$$AB + BC = AC, \quad AC + CB = AB, \quad BA + AC = BC.$$

If B is between A and C, the segments AB, BC, and AC have the same direction, and AC is obviously equal to the sum of the other two. The second and third equations can be found readily from the first. To obtain the second, we transpose BC and use the fact that $BC = -CB$. Thus

$$AB = AC - BC = AC + CB.$$

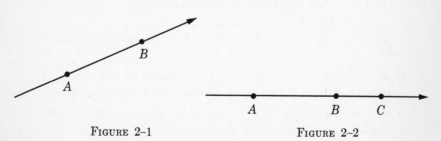

FIGURE 2–1   FIGURE 2–2

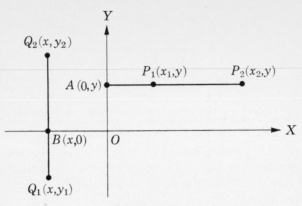

FIGURE 2–3

2–2 The distance between two points. In many problems the distance between two points of the coordinate plane is required. The distance between any two points, or the length of the line segment connecting them, can be determined from the coordinates of the points. We shall classify a line segment as *horizontal, vertical,* or *slant,* and derive appropriate formulas for the lengths of these kinds of segments. In making the derivations we shall use the idea of directed segments.

Let $P_1(x_1,y)$ and $P_2(x_2,y)$ be two points on a horizontal line, and let A be the point where the line cuts the y-axis (Fig. 2–3). We have

$$AP_1 + P_1P_2 = AP_2,$$
$$P_1P_2 = AP_2 - AP_1$$
$$= x_2 - x_1.$$

Similarly, for the vertical segment Q_1Q_2,

$$Q_1Q_2 = Q_1B + BQ_2,$$
$$= BQ_2 - BQ_1$$
$$= y_2 - y_1.$$

Hence the directed distance from a first point to a second point on a horizontal line is equal to the abscissa of the second point minus the abscissa of the first point. The distance is positive or negative according as the second point is to the right or left of the first point. A similar statement can be made relative to a vertical segment.

Inasmuch as the lengths of segments, without regard to direction, are often desired, we state a rule which gives results as positive quantities.

RULE. *The length of a horizontal segment joining two points is the abscissa of the point on the right minus the abscissa of the point on the left.*

The length of a vertical segment joining two points is the ordinate of the upper point minus the ordinate of the lower point.

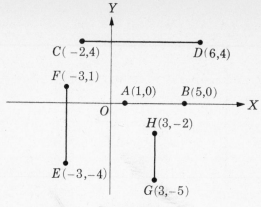

FIGURE 2-4

We apply this rule to find the lengths of the segments in Fig. 2–4.

$$AB = 5 - 1 = 4, \qquad\qquad CD = 6 - (-2) = 6 + 2 = 8,$$
$$EF = 1 - (-4) = 1 + 4 = 5, \quad GH = -2 - (-5) = -2 + 5 = 3.$$

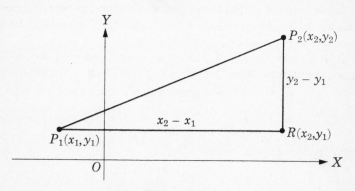

FIGURE 2-5

We next consider two points which determine a slant line. Let the points be $P_1(x_1, y_1)$ and $P_2(x_2, y_2)$. Draw a line through P_1 parallel to the x-axis and a line through P_2 parallel to the y-axis (Fig. 2–5). These two lines intersect at the point R, whose abscissa is x_2 and whose ordinate is y_1. Hence

$$P_1R = x_2 - x_1 \qquad \text{and} \qquad RP_2 = y_2 - y_1.$$

By the Pythagorean theorem,

$$(P_1P_2)^2 = (x_2 - x_1)^2 + (y_2 - y_1)^2.$$

Denoting the length of P_1P_2 by d, we have

$$d = \sqrt{(x_2 - x_1)^2 + (y_2 - y_1)^2}.$$

The positive square root is chosen because we shall usually be interested only in the magnitude of the segment.   We state this distance formula in words.

THEOREM.   *To find the distance between two points, add the square of the difference of the abscissas to the square of the difference of the ordinates and take the positive square root of the sum.*

In employing the distance formula either point may be designated by (x_1, y_1) and the other by (x_2, y_2).   This results from the fact that the two differences involved are squared.   The square of the difference of two numbers is unchanged when the order of the subtraction is reversed.

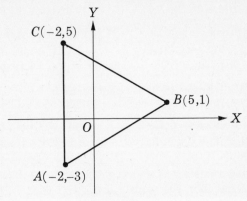

FIGURE 2-6

EXAMPLE.   Find the lengths of the sides of the triangle with the vertices $A(-2,-3)$, $B(5,1)$, and $C(-2,5)$.

Solution.   The abscissas of A and C are the same, and therefore side AC is vertical.   The other sides are slant segments.   The length of the vertical side is the difference of the ordinates.   The distance formula yields the lengths of the other sides.   Thus we get

$$AC = 5 - (-3) = 5 + 3 = 8,$$
$$AB = \sqrt{(5 + 2)^2 + (1 + 3)^2} = \sqrt{65},$$
$$BC = \sqrt{(5 + 2)^2 + (1 - 5)^2} = \sqrt{65}.$$

The lengths show that the triangle is isosceles.

EXERCISE 2-1

1. Plot the points $A(1,0)$, $B(3,0)$, and $C(7,0)$.   Then find the following directed segments: AB, AC, BC, BA, CA, and CB.

2. Given the points $A(2,-3)$, $B(2,1)$, and $C(2,5)$, find the directed distances AB, BA, AC, CA, BC, and CB.

3. Plot the points $A(-1,0)$, $B(2,0)$, and $C(5,0)$, and verify the following equations by numerical substitutions: $AB + BC = AC$; $AC + CB = AB$; $BA + AC = BC$.

Find the distance between the pairs of points in problems 4 through 9:

4. $(1,3)$, $(4,7)$.   5. $(-3,4)$, $(2,-8)$.

6. $(-2,-3)$, $(1,0)$.   7. $(5,-12)$, $(0,0)$.

8. $(0,-4)$, $(3,0)$.   9. $(2,7)$, $(-1,4)$.

In each problem 10–13 draw the triangle with the given vertices and find the lengths of the sides:

10. $A(1,-1)$, $B(4,-1)$, $C(4,3)$.   11. $A(-1,1)$, $B(2,3)$, $C(0,4)$.

12. $A(0,0)$, $B(2,-3)$, $C(-2,5)$.   13. $A(0,-3)$, $B(3,0)$, $C(0,-4)$.

Draw the triangles in problems 14–17 and show that each is isosceles:

14. $A(-2,1)$, $B(2,-4)$, $C(6,1)$.   15. $A(-1,3)$, $B(3,0)$, $C(6,4)$.

16. $A(8,3)$, $B(1,-1)$, $C(1,7)$.   17. $A(-4,4)$, $B(-3,-3)$, $C(3,3)$.

Show that the triangles 18–21 are right triangles:

18. $A(1,3)$, $B(10,5)$, $C(2,1)$.   19. $A(-3,1)$, $B(4,-2)$, $C(2,3)$.

20. $A(0,3)$, $B(-3,-4)$, $C(2,-2)$.   21. $A(4,-3)$, $B(3,4)$, $C(0,0)$.

22. Show that $A(-\sqrt{3},1)$, $B(2\sqrt{3},-2)$, and $C(2\sqrt{3},4)$ are vertices of an equilateral triangle.

23. Given the points $A(1,1)$, $B(5,4)$, $C(2,8)$, and $D(-2,5)$, show that the quadrilateral $ABCD$ has all its sides equal.

Determine if the points in each problem 24–27 lie on a straight line:

24. $(3,0)$, $(0,-2)$, $(9,4)$.   25. $(2,1)$, $(-1,2)$, $(5,0)$.

26. $(-4,0)$, $(0,2)$, $(9,7)$.   27. $(-1,-1)$, $(6,-4)$, $(-11,8)$.

28. If the point $(x,3)$ is equidistant from $(3,-2)$ and $(7,4)$, find x.

29. Find the point on the y-axis which is equidistant from $(-5,-2)$ and $(3,2)$.

2–3 Inclination and slope of a line. If a line intersects the x-axis, the inclination of the line is defined as the angle whose initial side extends to the right along the x-axis and whose terminal side is upward along the line.* In Fig. 2–7 the angle θ is the inclination of the line, MX is the initial side, and ML is the terminal side. The inclination of a line parallel to the x-axis is 0°. The inclination of a slant line is a positive angle less than 180°.

The *slope* of a line is defined as the tangent of its angle of inclination. A line which leans to the right has a positive slope because the inclination is an acute angle. The slopes of lines which lean to the left are negative.

---

* When an angle is measured from the first side to the second side, the first side is called the initial side and the second side is called the terminal side. Further, the angle is positive or negative according as it is measured in a counterclockwise or a clockwise direction.

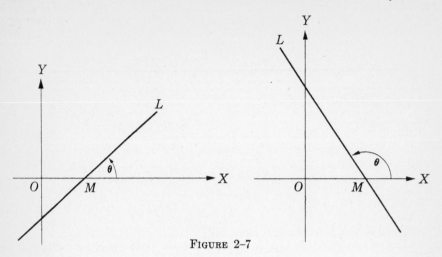

FIGURE 2–7

The slope of a horizontal line is zero.   Vertical lines do not have a slope, however, since 90° has no tangent.

If the inclination of a nonvertical line is known, the slope can be determined by the use of a table of trigonometric functions.   Conversely, if the slope of a line is known, its inclination can be found.   In most problems, however, it is more convenient to deal with the slope of a line rather than with its inclination.

The following theorem is a direct consequence of the definition of slope.

THEOREM.   *Two nonvertical lines are parallel if and only if their slopes are equal.*

If the coordinates of two points on a line are known, we may find the slope of the line from the given coordinates.   We now derive a formula for this purpose.

Let $P_1(x_1,y_1)$ and $P_2(x_2,y_2)$ be the two given points, and indicate the slope by m.   Then, referring to Fig. 2–8, we have

$$m = \tan \theta = \frac{RP_2}{P_1R} = \frac{y_2 - y_1}{x_2 - x_1}.$$

FIGURE 2–8

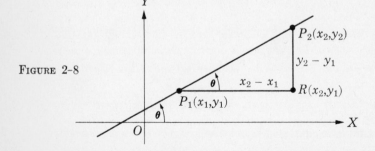

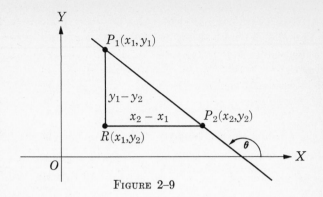

FIGURE 2–9

If the line slants to the left, as in Fig. 2–9,

$$m = \tan \theta = -\frac{y_1 - y_2}{x_2 - x_1} = \frac{y_2 - y_1}{x_2 - x_1}.$$

Hence the slope is determined in the same way for lines slanting either to the left or to the right.

THEOREM. *The slope m of a line passing through two given points $P_1(x_1,y_1)$ and $P_2(x_2,y_2)$ is equal to the difference of the ordinates divided by the difference of the abscissas taken in the same order; that is*

$$\boldsymbol{m = \frac{y_2 - y_1}{x_2 - x_1}.}$$

This formula yields the slope if the two points determine a slant line. If the line is vertical, the denominator is zero. Hence a slope is not defined for a vertical line. Conversely, if the denominator is equal to zero, the points are on a vertical line. We observe, further, that either of the points may be regarded as $P_1(x_1,y_1)$ and the other as $P_2(x_2,y_2)$, since

$$\frac{y_2 - y_1}{x_2 - x_1} = \frac{y_1 - y_2}{x_1 - x_2}.$$

EXAMPLE. Given the points $A(-2,-1)$, $B(4,0)$, $C(3,3)$, and $D(-3,2)$, show that $ABCD$ is a parallelogram.

Solution. We determine from the slopes of the sides if the figure is a parallelogram.

$$\text{Slope of } AB = \frac{0 - (-1)}{4 - (-2)} = \frac{1}{6}, \quad \text{slope of } BC = \frac{3 - 0}{3 - 4} = -3,$$

$$\text{slope of } CD = \frac{2 - 3}{-3 - 3} = \frac{1}{6}, \quad \text{slope of } DA = \frac{2 - (-1)}{-3 - (-2)} = -3.$$

The opposite sides have equal slopes, and therefore $ABCD$ is a parallelogram.

2–4 Angle between two lines. Two intersecting lines form four angles. There are two pairs of equal angles, and an angle of one pair is the supplement of an angle of the other pair. We shall show how to find a measure of each angle in terms of the slopes of the lines. Noticing Fig. 2–10 and recalling that an exterior angle of a triangle is equal to the sum of the two remote interior angles, we see that

$$\phi + \theta_1 = \theta_2 \qquad \text{or} \qquad \phi = \theta_2 - \theta_1.$$

Using the formula for the tangent of the difference of two angles, we find

$$\tan \phi = \tan (\theta_2 - \theta_1) = \frac{\tan \theta_2 - \tan \theta_1}{1 + \tan \theta_1 \tan \theta_2}.$$

If we let $m_2 = \tan \theta_2$ and $m_1 = \tan \theta_1$, then we have

$$\tan \phi = \frac{m_2 - m_1}{1 + m_1 m_2},$$

where m_2 is the slope of the terminal side, m_1 is the slope of the initial side, and ϕ is measured in a counterclockwise direction.

The angle ψ is the supplement of ϕ, and therefore

$$\tan \psi = -\tan \phi = \frac{m_1 - m_2}{1 + m_1 m_2}.$$

This formula for $\tan \psi$ is the same as that for $\tan \phi$ except that the terms in the numerator are reversed. We observe from the diagram, however, that the terminal side of ψ is the initial side of ϕ and that the initial side of ψ is the terminal side of ϕ, as indicated by the counterclockwise arrows. Hence, in terms of the slopes of initial and terminal sides, the tangent of either angle may be found by the same rule. We state this conclusion as a theorem.

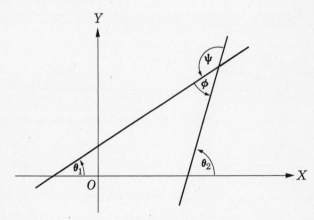

FIGURE 2–10

THEOREM. *If ϕ is an angle, measured counterclockwise, between two lines, then*

$$\tan \phi = \frac{m_2 - m_1}{1 + m_1 m_2}, \tag{1}$$

where m_2 is the slope of the terminal side and m_1 is the slope of the initial side.

This formula will not apply if either of the lines is vertical, since a slope is not defined for a vertical line.   For this case, the problem would be that of finding the angle, or function of the angle, which a line of known slope makes with the vertical.   Hence no new formula is necessary.

For any two slant lines which are not perpendicular formula (1) will yield a definite number as the value of $\tan \phi$.   Conversely, if the formula yields a definite number, the lines are not perpendicular.   Hence we conclude that the lines are perpendicular when, and only when, the denominator of the formula is equal to zero.   The relation $1 + m_1 m_2 = 0$ may be written in the form

$$m_2 = -\frac{1}{m_1},$$

which expresses one slope as the negative reciprocal of the other slope.

THEOREM. *Two slant lines are perpendicular if, and only if, the slope of one is the negative reciprocal of the slope of the other.*

EXAMPLE. Find the tangents of the angles of the triangle whose vertices are $A(-2,3)$, $B(8,-5)$, and $C(5,4)$. Find each angle to the nearest degree. (See Table II of the Appendix.)

Solution. The slopes of the sides are indicated in Fig. 2–11. Substituting in formula (1), we get

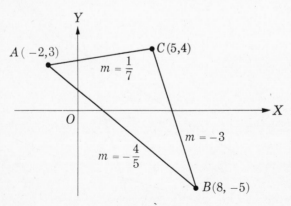

FIGURE 2–11

$$\tan A = \frac{\frac{1}{7} - (-\frac{4}{5})}{1 + (-\frac{4}{5})(\frac{1}{7})} = \frac{33}{31} = 1.06, \qquad A = 47°,$$

$$\tan B = \frac{-\frac{4}{5} - (-3)}{1 + (-3)(-\frac{4}{5})} = \frac{11}{17} = .647, \qquad B = 33°,$$

$$\tan C = \frac{-3 - \frac{1}{7}}{1 + (\frac{1}{7})(-3)} = \frac{-22}{4} = -5.5, \qquad C = 100°.$$

EXERCISE 2-2

1. Give the slopes for the inclinations (a) 45°; (b) 0°; (c) 60°; (d) 120°; (e) 135°.

Find the slope of the line passing through the two points in each problem 2–7:

2. (2,3), (3,7).   3. (6,−13), (0,5).
4. (−4,8), (7,−3).   5. (5,4), (−3,−2).
6. (0,−9), (20,3).   7. (4,12), (−8,−1).

8. Show that each of the following sets of four points are vertices of a parallelogram $ABCD$:

(a) $A(2,1)$, $B(6,1)$, $C(4,4)$, $D(0,4)$.
(b) $A(−3,2)$, $B(5,0)$, $C(4,−3)$, $D(−4,−1)$.
(c) $A(0,−3)$, $B(4,−7)$, $C(12,−2)$, $D(8,2)$.
(d) $A(−2,0)$, $B(4,2)$, $C(7,7)$, $D(1,5)$.

9. Verify that each triangle with the given points as vertices is a right triangle by showing that the slope of one of the sides is the negative reciprocal of the slope of another side:

(a) $(5,−4)$, $(5,4)$, $(1,0)$.   (b) $(−1,1)$, $(3,−7)$, $(3,3)$.
(c) $(8,1)$, $(1,−2)$, $(6,−4)$.   (d) $(−1,−5)$, $(6,−7)$, $(3,9)$.
(e) $(0,0)$, $(3,−2)$, $(2,3)$.   (f) $(0,0)$, $(17,0)$, $(1,4)$.

10. In each of the following sets, show that the four points are vertices of a rectangle:

(a) $(−6,3)$, $(−2,−2)$, $(3,2)$, $(−1,7)$.   (b) $(1,2)$, $(6,−3)$, $(9,0)$, $(4,5)$.
(c) $(0,0)$, $(2,6)$, $(−1,7)$, $(−3,1)$.   (d) $(5,−2)$, $(7,5)$, $(0,7)$, $(−2,0)$.
(e) $(3,2)$, $(2,9)$, $(−5,8)$, $(−4,1)$.   (f) $(5,6)$, $(1,0)$, $(4,−2)$, $(8,4)$.

11. Using slopes, determine which of the following sets of three points lie on a straight line:

(a) $(3,0)$, $(0,−2)$, $(9,4)$.   (b) $(2,1)$, $(−1,2)$, $(5,0)$.
(c) $(−4,0)$, $(0,2)$, $(9,7)$.   (d) $(−1,−1)$, $(6,−4)$, $(−11,8)$.

Find the tangents of the angles of the triangle ABC in each problem 12–15. Find the angles to the nearest degrees.

12. $A(−3,−1)$, $B(3,3)$, $C(−1,1)$.

13. $A(−1,1)$, $B(2,3)$, $C(7,−7)$.

14. $A(−3,1)$, $B(4,2)$, $C(2,3)$.

15. $A(0,3)$, $B(−3,−4)$, $C(2,−2)$.

16. The line through the points (4,3) and (−6,0) intersects the line through (0,0) and (−1,5). Find the intersection angles.

17. Two lines passing through (2,3) make an angle of 45°. If the slope of one of the lines is 2, find the slope of the other. Two solutions.

18. What angle does a line of slope $-\frac{2}{3}$ make with a vertical line?

2–5 The mid-point of a line segment. Problems in geometry make much use of the mid-points of line segments. We shall derive formulas which give the coordinates of the point midway between two points of given coordinates.

Let $P_1(x_1,y_1)$ and $P_2(x_2,y_2)$ be the extremities of a line segment, and let $P(x,y)$ be the mid-point of P_1P_2. From similar triangles (Fig. 2–12), we have

$$\frac{P_1P}{P_1P_2} = \frac{P_1M}{P_1N} = \frac{MP}{NP_2} = \tfrac{1}{2}.$$

Hence

$$\frac{P_1M}{P_1N} = \frac{x - x_1}{x_2 - x_1} = \tfrac{1}{2} \quad \text{and} \quad \frac{MP}{NP_2} = \frac{y - y_1}{y_2 - y_1} = \tfrac{1}{2}.$$

Solving for x and y gives

$$x = \frac{x_1 + x_2}{2}, \quad y = \frac{y_1 + y_2}{2}.$$

THEOREM.   *The abscissa of the mid-point of a line segment is half the sum of the abscissas of the end points; the ordinate is half the sum of the ordinates.*

This theorem may be generalized by letting $P(x,y)$ be any division point of the segment P_1P_2. Thus if

$$\frac{P_1P}{P_1P_2} = r,$$

then

$$\frac{x - x_1}{x_2 - x_1} = r \quad \text{and} \quad \frac{y - y_1}{y_2 - y_1} = r.$$

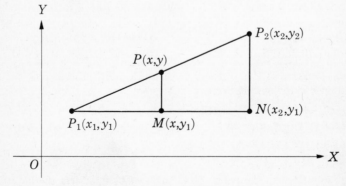

FIGURE 2–12

These equations give

$$x = x_1 + r(x_2 - x_1) \qquad \text{and} \qquad y = y_1 + r(y_2 - y_1).$$

If P is between P_1 and P_2, as in Fig. 2–12, the segments P_1P and P_1P_2 have the same direction, and the value of their ratio r is positive and less than 1. If P is on P_1P_2 extended through P_2, then r is greater than 1. If P is on the segment extended through P_1, the value of r is negative. The converse of each of these statements is true.

EXAMPLE.   Find the mid-point and the trisection point nearer P_2 of the segment determined by $P_1(-3,6)$ and $P_2(5,1)$.

Solution.

$$x = \frac{x_1 + x_2}{2} = \frac{-3 + 5}{2} = 1,$$

$$y = \frac{y_1 + y_2}{2} = \frac{6 + 1}{2} = \frac{7}{2}.$$

For the trisection point we use $r = \frac{2}{3}$.

$$x = x_1 + r(x_2 - x_1) = -3 + \tfrac{2}{3}(5 + 3) = \tfrac{7}{3},$$
$$y = y_1 + r(y_2 - y_1) = 6 + \tfrac{2}{3}(1 - 6) = \tfrac{8}{3}.$$

2–6 Analytic proofs of geometric theorems.   By the use of a coordinate system many of the theorems of elementary geometry can be proved with surprising simplicity and directness.   We illustrate the procedure in the following example.

EXAMPLE.   Prove that the diagonals of a parallelogram bisect each other.

Solution.   We first draw a parallelogram and then introduce a coordinate system.   A judicious location of the axes relative to the figure makes the writing of the coordinates of the vertices easier and also simplifies the algebraic operations involved in making the proof.   Therefore we choose a vertex as the origin and a coordinate axis along a side of the parallelogram (Fig. 2–13).   Then we write the

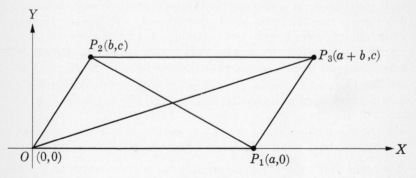

FIGURE 2–13

coordinates of the vertices as $O(0,0)$, $P_1(a,0)$, $P_2(b,c)$, and $P_3(a + b,c)$. It is essential that the coordinates of P_2 and P_3 express the fact that P_2P_3 is equal and parallel to OP_1. This is achieved by making the ordinates of P_2 and P_3 the same and making the abscissa of P_3 exceed the abscissa of P_2 by a.

To show that OP_3 and P_1P_2 bisect each other, we find the coordinates of the mid-point of each diagonal.

$$\text{Mid-point of } OP_3\text{:} \quad x = \frac{a + b}{2}, \quad y = \frac{c}{2}.$$

$$\text{Mid-point of } P_1P_2\text{:} \quad x = \frac{a + b}{2}, \quad y = \frac{c}{2}.$$

Since the mid-point of each diagonal is $\left(\dfrac{a + b}{2}, \dfrac{c}{2}\right)$, the theorem is proved.

Note. In making a proof by this method it is essential that a general figure be used. For example, neither a rectangle nor a rhombus (a parallelogram with all sides equal) should be used for a parallelogram. A proof of a theorem based on a special case would not constitute a general proof.

Exercise 2-3

1. Find the mid-point of AB in each of the following:

    (a) $A(-2,5)$, $B(4,-7)$;   (b) $A(7,-3)$, $B(-3,9)$;

    (c) $A(-7,12)$, $B(11,0)$;   (d) $A(0,-7)$, $B(3,10)$.

2. The vertices of a triangle are $A(7,1)$, $B(-1,6)$, and $C(3,0)$. Find the coordinates of the mid-points of the sides.

3. The points $A(-1,-4)$, $B(7,2)$, $C(5,6)$, and $D(-5,8)$ are vertices of the quadrilateral $ABCD$. Find the coordinates of the mid-point of each line segment connecting the mid-points of opposite sides.

Find the trisection points of the segment AB:

    4. $A(-9,-6)$, $B(9,6)$.   5. $A(-5,6)$, $B(7,0)$.

    6. $A(-4,3)$, $B(8,-3)$.   7. $A(-1,0)$, $B(4,6)$.

8. The points $A(2,2)$, $B(6,0)$, and $C(10,8)$ are vertices of a triangle. Determine if the medians are concurrent by finding the point on each median which is $\frac{2}{3}$ of the way from the vertex to the other extremity. (A median of a triangle is a line segment joining a vertex and the mid-point of the opposite side.)

9. The points $A(2,1)$, $B(6,-3)$, and $C(4,5)$ are vertices of a triangle. Find the trisection point on each median which is nearer the opposite side.

10. The line segment joining $A(-3,2)$ and $B(5,-3)$ is extended through each end by a length equal to its original length. Find the coordinates of the new ends.

11. The line segment joining $A(-4,-1)$ and $B(3,6)$ is doubled in length by having half its length added at each end. Find the coordinates of the new ends.

The points P_1, P_2, and P are on a straight line in each problem 12–15. Find r, the ratio of P_1P to P_1P_2.

12. $P_1(-1,-3)$, $P_2(5,1)$, $P(2,-1)$.   13. $P_1(3,1)$, $P_2(6,3)$, $P(9,5)$.

14. $P_1(2,1)$, $P_2(5,-1)$, $P(-1,3)$.   15. $P_1(-4,2)$, $P_2(1,-2)$, $P(11,-10)$.

Give analytic proofs of the following theorems:

16. The diagonals of the rectangle are equal. [*Suggestion:* Choose the axes so that the vertices of the rectangle are $(0,0)$, $(a,0)$, $(0,b)$, and (a,b).]

17. The mid-point of the hypotenuse of a right triangle is equidistant from the three vertices.

18. The line segment joining the mid-points of two sides of a triangle is parallel to the third side and equal to half of it.

19. The diagonals of an isosceles trapezoid are equal. [*Hint:* Notice that the axes may be placed so that the coordinates of the vertices are $(0,0)$, $(a,0)$, (b,c), and $(a-b,c)$.]

20. The segment joining the mid-points of the nonparallel sides of a trapezoid is parallel to and equal to half the sum of the parallel sides.

21. The segments which join the mid-points of the sides of any quadrilateral, if taken in order, form a parallelogram.

22. The line segments which join the mid-points of the opposite sides of a quadrilateral bisect each other.

23. The diagonals of a rhombus are perpendicular and bisect each other.

24. The sum of the squares of the sides of a parallelogram is equal to the sum of the squares of the diagonals.

25. The lines drawn from a vertex of a parallelogram to the mid-points of the opposite sides trisect a diagonal.

26. The medians of a triangle meet in a point which lies two-thirds of the way from each vertex to the mid-point of the opposite side.

CHAPTER 3

THE STRAIGHT LINE

3–1 Introduction. The straight line is the simplest geometric curve. Despite its simplicity, the line is a vital concept of mathematics and enters into our daily experiences in numerous interesting and useful ways. In Section 1–7 we stated that the graph of a first degree equation in x and y is a straight line; we shall now establish that statement. Furthermore, we shall write linear equations in different forms such that each reveals useful information concerning the location of the line which it represents.

3–2 The locus of a first degree equation. The equation

$$Ax + By + C = 0, \tag{1}$$

where A, B, and C are constants with A and B not both zero, is a general equation of the first degree. We shall prove that the locus, or graph, of this equation is a straight line by showing that all points of the locus lie on a line and that the coordinates of all points of the line satisfy the equation.

Let $P_1(x_1,y_1)$ and $P_2(x_2,y_2)$ be any two points of the graph; that is,

$$Ax_1 + By_1 + C = 0, \tag{a}$$
$$Ax_2 + By_2 + C = 0. \tag{b}$$

By subtraction, these equations yield

$$A(x_1 - x_2) + B(y_1 - y_2) = 0,$$
$$B(y_1 - y_2) = -A(x_1 - x_2),$$

and if $B \neq 0$,

$$\frac{y_1 - y_2}{x_1 - x_2} = -\frac{A}{B}.$$

The last equation shows that the slope of a line passing through two points of the graph is $-(A/B)$. Therefore if $P_3(x_3,y_3)$ is any other point of the locus, the slope of the segment P_1P_3 is also $-(A/B)$. From the equality of these slopes we conclude that P_1, P_2, and P_3, and hence all points of the locus, lie on a line. To determine if the graph consists of all points of this line, we need to show that the coordinates of any other point of the line satisfy the given equation (1). Denoting a point of the line by $P_4(x_4,y_4)$, we have

$$\frac{y_4 - y_1}{x_4 - x_1} = -\frac{A}{B}.$$

31

By clearing of fractions and transposing terms, this equation takes the form

$$Ax_4 + By_4 - Ax_1 - By_1 = 0.$$

From equation (a), $-Ax_1 - By_1 = C$, and hence

$$Ax_4 + By_4 + C = 0.$$

The point (x_4, y_4) satisfies the given equation. This completes the proof except for the case in which $B = 0$. For this value of B equation (1) reduces to

$$x = -\frac{C}{A}.$$

The coordinates of all points, and only those points, having the abscissa $-(C/A)$ satisfy this equation. Hence the locus is a line parallel to the y-axis and located $-(C/A)$ units from the axis.

THEOREM. *The locus of the equation $Ax + By + C = 0$, where A, B, and C are constants with A and B not both zero, is a straight line. If $B = 0$, the line is vertical; otherwise the slope is $-(A/B)$.*

3–3 Special forms of the first degree equation. We shall now convert equation (1) to other forms and interpret the coefficients geometrically. Solving for y gives, where $B \neq 0$,

$$y = -\frac{A}{B} x - \frac{C}{B}.$$

The coefficient of x, as we have seen, is the slope of the line. By setting $x = 0$, we notice that the constant term is the y-intercept. Substituting m for the slope and b for the y-intercept, we obtain the simpler form

$$y = mx + b. \tag{2}$$

This is called the *slope-intercept form* of the equation of a line. An equation in this form makes evident the slope and the y-intercept of the line which it represents. Conversely, the equation of a line of given slope and y-intercept may be written at once by substituting the proper values for m and b.

Illustration. The equation of the line of slope -2 and passing through $(0,5)$ is $y = -2x + 5$.

We next express equation (1) in a form which gives prominence to the x-intercept and the y-intercept. We have

$$Ax + By = -C,$$

$$\frac{Ax}{-C} + \frac{By}{-C} = 1, \quad \text{or} \quad \frac{x}{-C/A} + \frac{y}{-C/B} = 1.$$

The denominator of x in the last equation is the x-intercept and the denominator of y is the y-intercept.   If we let a and b stand for the intercepts, we have the equation

$$\frac{x}{a} + \frac{y}{b} = 1. \tag{3}$$

This is called the *intercept form* of the equation of a straight line.   It may be used when the intercepts are different from zero.

Equation (2) represents a line passing through $(0,b)$.   The equation may be altered slightly to focus attention on any other point of the line. If the line passes through (x_1,y_1), we have

$$y_1 = mx_1 + b, \quad \text{and} \quad b = y_1 - mx_1.$$

Substituting for b gives

$$y = mx + y_1 - mx_1,$$

and hence

$$y - y_1 = m(x - x_1). \tag{4}$$

Equation (4) is called the *point-slope form* of the equation of a line.

If the line of equation (4) passes through the point (x_2,y_2), then

$$m = \frac{y_2 - y_1}{x_2 - x_1},$$

and we have

$$y - y_1 = \frac{y_2 - y_1}{x_2 - x_1} (x - x_1). \tag{5}$$

It can readily be seen that the graph of this equation passes through the points (x_1,y_1) and (x_2,y_2).   This form is called the *two-point form* of the equation of a straight line.

The equations (2)–(5) do not apply when the line is vertical.   In this case m is not defined, and neither could we substitute properly for the intercepts in the forms (2) and (3).   The equation of a vertical line can be written immediately, however, if any point of the line is known.   Thus a vertical line through (x_1,y_1) has the abscissa x_1 for all points of the line. Hence the equation is

$$x = x_1.$$

A horizontal line through (x_1,y_1) has $m = 0$, and equation (4) applies. Of course, the ordinates are all the same on a horizontal line, and we could write the equation directly as

$$y = y_1.$$

Illustrations. If a line cuts the coordinate axes so that the x-intercept is 3 and the y-intercept is -5, its equation by formula (3) is

$$\frac{x}{3} + \frac{y}{-5} = 1, \qquad \text{or} \qquad 5x - 3y = 15.$$

The equation of the line through $(-1,4)$ with slope 3 is, by the point-slope form,

$$y - 4 = 3(x + 1), \qquad \text{or} \qquad 3x - y + 7 = 0.$$

To obtain the equation of the line through $(-3,5)$ and $(4,1)$, we substitute in formula (5), and have

$$y - 5 = \frac{1 - 5}{4 + 3}(x + 3).$$

Whence, simplifying,

$$7y - 35 = -4x - 12, \qquad \text{or} \qquad 4x + 7y = 23.$$

The illustrations show that formulas (2)–(5) can be employed to write, quickly and simply, equations of lines which pass through two given points or through one known point with a given slope. The inverse problem, that of drawing the graph of a linear equation in x and y, is likewise simple. Since the locus is a straight line, two points are sufficient for constructing the graph. For this purpose the intercepts on the axes are usually the most convenient. For example, we find the intercepts of the equation $3x - 4y = 12$ to be $a = 4$ and $b = -3$. Hence the graph is the line drawn through $(4,0)$ and $(0,-3)$. The intercepts are not sufficient for drawing a line which passes through the origin. For this case the intercepts a and b are both zero. Hence a point other than the origin is necessary.

We have seen that the slope of the line corresponding to the equation $Ax + By + C = 0$ is $-(A/B)$. That is, the slope is obtained from the equation by dividing the coefficient of x by the coefficient of y and reversing the sign of the result. Hence we can readily determine if the lines represented by two equations are parallel, perpendicular, or if they intersect obliquely. Lines are parallel if their slopes are equal, and we recall that two lines are perpendicular if the slope of one is the negative of the reciprocal of the slope of the other.

EXAMPLE 1. Find the equation of the line which passes through $(-1,3)$ and is parallel to $4x + 3y = 2$.

Solution. We shall show two ways for finding the required equation. First, from the given equation, the slope is seen to be $-(\frac{4}{3})$. Substituting this slope value and the coordinates of the given point in the point-slope formula, we have

$$y - 3 = -\tfrac{4}{3}(x + 1),$$

or

$$4x + 3y = 5.$$

Alternatively, we notice that $4x + 3y = D$ is parallel to the given line for any real value of D. To determine D so that the line shall pass through $(-1,3)$, we substitute these coordinates for x and y and obtain

$$4(-1) + 3(3) = D, \quad \text{or} \quad D = 5.$$

By using 5 for D, we have again the equation $4x + 3y = 5$.

EXAMPLE 2. A point moves so that it is equally distant from the two points $A(3,2)$ and $B(5,6)$. Find the equation of its locus.

Solution. From plane geometry we know that the locus is the line perpendicular to the segment AB and passing through its mid-point. The slope of AB is 2, and the coordinates of the mid-point are $(4,4)$. The required slope is $-\frac{1}{2}$. Hence we write $x + 2y = D$. This equation has the proper slope, and we need to determine D so that the line shall pass through $(4,4)$. Substituting, we get

$$x + 2y = 4 + 2(4) = 12.$$

The required equation, therefore, is $x + 2y = 12$. We could also obtain this equation by using the point-slope form (4).

EXERCISE 3–1

By solving for y, write each equation 1–12 in the slope-intercept form. In each case give the value of the slope m and the value of the y-intercept b. Draw the lines.

1. $3x + y = 6$.
2. $3x - y - 3 = 0$.
3. $4x - 2y = 3$.
4. $6x + 3y = 5$.
5. $x + 2y + 4 = 0$.
6. $x - 5y = 10$.
7. $4x - 3y = 0$.
8. $2x + 7y = 0$.
9. $5x + 3y = 7$.
10. $x - 8y = 4$.
11. $7x - 11y = 9$.
12. $x + y = 6$.

By inspection, give the slope and intercepts of each line represented by equations 13–24.

13. $4x - y = 12$.
14. $x - y = 7$.
15. $x + y + 4 = 0$.
16. $4x + 9y = 36$.
17. $3x - 4y = 12$.
18. $6x - 3y - 10 = 0$.
19. $x + 7y = 11$.
20. $2x + 3y = 14$.
21. $7x + 3y + 6 = 0$.
22. $3x - 8y = 5$.
23. $8x + 3y = 4$.
24. $3x + 3y = 1$.

In each problem 25–36, write the equation of the line determined by the slope m and the y-intercept b.

25. $m = 3; b = -4$.
26. $m = 2; b = 3$.
27. $m = -4; b = 5$.
28. $m = -1; b = 1$.
29. $m = \frac{2}{3}; b = -2$.
30. $m = \frac{3}{2}; b = -6$.
31. $m = 0; b = -6$.
32. $m = -5; b = 0$.
33. $m = -\frac{7}{2}; b = -8$.
34. $m = 0; b = -2$.
35. $m = 0; b = 0$.
36. $m = -\frac{3}{8}; b = 0$.

Write the equation of the line which has the x-intercept a and the y-intercept b in each problem 37–48.

37. $a = 3, b = 2$.   38. $a = 5, b = 1$.

39. $a = 4, b = -3$.   40. $a = 7, b = -5$.

41. $a = -2, b = -2$.   42. $a = -1, b = -1$.

43. $a = \frac{2}{3}, b = \frac{1}{2}$.   44. $a = -\frac{3}{2}; b = 1$.

45. $a = \frac{11}{3}; b = \frac{7}{2}$.   46. $a = \frac{9}{2}, b = -2$.

47. $a = -\frac{2}{3}, b = -\frac{11}{2}$.   48. $a = \frac{3}{4}, b = \frac{4}{3}$.

In each equation 49–60, write the equation of the line which passes through the point A with the slope m.   Draw the lines.

49. $A(3,1); m = 2$.   50. $A(-3,-5); m = 1$.

51. $A(-2,0); m = \frac{2}{3}$.   52. $A(0,-3); m = -4$.

53. $A(-3,-6); m = -\frac{1}{2}$.   54. $A(5,-2); m = -\frac{5}{2}$.

55. $A(0,3); m = 0$.   56. $A(3,0); m = 0$.

57. $A(0,0); m = -\frac{8}{3}$.   58. $A(0,0); m = \frac{2}{7}$.

59. $A(-5,-7); m = -6$.   60. $A(9,1); m = -\frac{1}{7}$.

Find the equation of the line determined by the points A and B in each problem 61–72.   Check the answers by substitutions.

61. $A(3,-1); B(-4,5)$.   62. $A(1,5); B(4,1)$.

63. $A(0,2); B(4,-6)$.   64. $A(-2,-4); B(3,3)$.

65. $A(3,-2); B(3,7)$.   66. $A(0,0); B(3,-4)$.

67. $A(5,-\frac{2}{3}); B(\frac{1}{2},-2)$.   68. $A(\frac{1}{2},5); B(-2,5)$.

69. $A(0,1); B(0,0)$.   70. $A(3,0); B(4,0)$.

71. $A(-1,-1); B(-2,-3)$.   72. $A(\frac{1}{2},1); B(-1,\frac{3}{2})$.

73. Show that $Ax + By = D_1$ and $Bx - Ay = D_2$ are equations of perpendicular lines.

74. Show that the graphs of the equations

$$Ax + By = D_1,$$
$$Ax + By = D_2$$

are (a) the same if $D_1 = D_2$; (b) parallel lines if $D_1 \neq D_2$.

In each problem 75–84 find the equations of two lines through A, one parallel and the other perpendicular to the line corresponding to the given equation. Draw the lines.

75. $A(4,1); 2x - 3y + 5 = 0$.   76. $A(-1,2); 2x - y = 0$.

77. $A(3,4); 7x + 5y + 4 = 0$.   78. $A(0,0); x - y = 3$.

79. $A(2,-3); 8x - y = 0$.   80. $A(0,6); 2x - 2y = 1$.

81. $A(-1,1); y = 1$.   82. $A(3,5); x = 0$.

83. $A(7,0); 9x + y - 3 = 0$.   84. $A(-4,0); 4x + 3y = 3$.

85. The vertices of a triangle are $A(1,0)$, $B(9,2)$, and $C(3,6)$.   Find the following:

   (a) the equations of the sides;
   (b) the equations of the medians and the coordinates of their common point;
   (c) the equations of the altitudes and the coordinates of their common point;
   (d) the equations of the perpendicular bisectors of the sides and the coordinates of their common point.

86. The vertices of a triangle are $A(-2,3)$, $B(6,-6)$, and $C(8,0)$.   Find the equations of the lines and the coordinates of the points pertaining to this triangle which are called for in problem 85.

3–4 The distance from a line to a point.   The distance from a line to a point can be found from the equation of the line and the coordinates of the point.   We shall derive a formula for this purpose.   We observe first that the distance from a vertical line to a point is immediately obtainable by taking the difference of the abscissa of the point and the x-intercept of the line.   Hence no additional formula is needed for this case.

Let the equation of a slant line be written in the form

$$Ax + By + C = 0, \tag{1}$$

and let $P_1(x_1,y_1)$ be any point not on the line.   Since the line is a slant line, $B \neq 0$.   Consider now the line through P_1 parallel to the given line, and the line through the origin perpendicular to the given line, whose equations respectively are

$$Ax + By + C' = 0, \tag{2}$$
$$Bx - Ay = 0. \tag{3}$$

The required distance d (Fig. 3–1) is equal to the segment PQ, where P and Q are the intersection points of the perpendicular line and the parallel lines.   The simultaneous solutions of equations (1) and (3), and equations (2) and (3) give the intersection points

$$P\left(\frac{-AC}{A^2 + B^2}, \ \frac{-BC}{A^2 + B^2}\right), \quad Q\left(\frac{-AC'}{A^2 + B^2}, \ \frac{-BC'}{A^2 + B^2}\right).$$

We employ the formula for the distance between two points to find the length of PQ.   Thus

$$d^2 = (PQ)^2 = \frac{(C - C')^2 A^2}{(A^2 + B^2)^2} + \frac{(C - C')^2 B^2}{(A^2 + B^2)^2}$$
$$= \frac{(C - C')^2 (A^2 + B^2)}{(A^2 + B^2)^2} = \frac{(C - C')^2}{A^2 + B^2},$$

and

$$d = \frac{C - C'}{\pm\sqrt{A^2 + B^2}}.$$

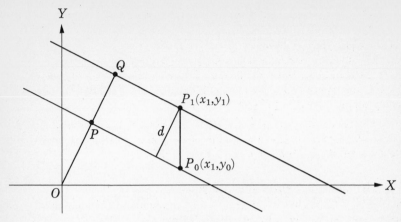

FIGURE 3–1

Since the line of equation (2) passes through $P_1(x_1,y_1)$, we have

$$Ax_1 + By_1 + C' = 0, \quad \text{and} \quad C' = -Ax_1 - By_1.$$

Hence, substituting for C',

$$d = \frac{Ax_1 + By_1 + C}{\pm\sqrt{A^2 + B^2}}.$$

To remove the ambiguity as to sign, we agree to give the radical in the denominator the sign of B. In other words, the sign of the denominator is selected so that the coefficient of y_1 is positive. A consequence of this choice of signs may be found by referring to the figure again, where P_0P_1 is parallel to the y-axis and $P_0(x_1,y_0)$ is a point of the given line. Since P_0 is a point on the line, we have

$$\frac{Ax_1 + By_0 + C}{\pm\sqrt{A^2 + B^2}} = 0.$$

Now if we replace y_0 by y_1 in the left side of this equation, we get an expression which is not equal to zero. The expression is positive if $y_1 > y_0$ and negative if $y_1 < y_0$. That is, the expression for d is positive if P_1 is above the line and negative if P_1 is below the line. We may therefore regard the distance from a line to a point as a directed distance.

The preceding discussion establishes the following theorem:

THEOREM. *The directed distance from the slant line $Ax + By + C = 0$ to the point $P_1(x_1,y_1)$ is given by the formula*

$$d = \frac{Ax_1 + By_1 + C}{\pm\sqrt{A^2 + B^2}}, \tag{4}$$

where the denominator is given the sign of B. The distance is positive if the point P_1 is above the line, and negative if P_1 is below the line.

3-4] THE DISTANCE FROM A LINE TO A POINT

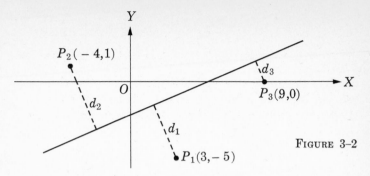

FIGURE 3–2

If equation (1) is divided by $\pm\sqrt{A^2 + B^2}$, the form

$$\frac{Ax + By + C}{\pm\sqrt{A^2 + B^2}} = 0$$

is obtained. This is called the *normal form* of the equation of a line. When an equation is in the normal form, the distance from the line to a point is given by substituting the coordinates of the point in the left member of the equation. By substituting the coordinates of the origin, the constant term is seen to be the perpendicular, or normal, distance to the origin.

EXAMPLE 1. Find the distance from the line $12y = 5x - 26$ to each of the points $P_1(3,-5)$, $P_2(-4,1)$, and $P_3(9,0)$.

Solution. We write the equation in the form $-5x + 12y + 26 = 0$. The required distances are then found by making substitutions in formula (4). Hence

$$d_1 = \frac{-5(3) + 12(-5) + 26}{\sqrt{5^2 + 12^2}} = -\frac{49}{13},$$

$$d_2 = \frac{-5(-4) + 12(1) + 26}{13} = \frac{58}{13},$$

$$d_3 = \frac{-5(9) + 12(0) + 26}{13} = -\frac{19}{13}.$$

The positive sign is used in the denominators because the coefficient of y is positive. The signs of the results show that P_1 and P_3 are below the line and that P_2 is above the line (Fig. 3–2).

EXAMPLE 2. Find the distance between the parallel lines $15x - 8y - 51 = 0$ and $15x - 8y + 68 = 0$.

Solution. The distance can be found by computing the distance from each line to a particular point. To minimize the computations, we find the distance from each line to the origin. Thus

$$d_1 = \frac{15(0) - 8(0) - 51}{-\sqrt{15^2 + 8^2}} = \frac{-51}{-17} = 3,$$

$$d_2 = \frac{15(0) - 8(0) + 68}{-17} = \frac{68}{-17} = -4.$$

The origin is 3 units above the first line and 4 units below the second line. Hence the lines are 7 units apart.

An alternate method for this problem would be to find the distance from one of the lines to a particular point on the other. The point $(0, 8.5)$ is on the second line, and using this point and the first equation, we find

$$d = \frac{15(0) - 8(8.5) - 51}{-17} = \frac{-119}{-17} = 7.$$

3–5 Families of lines. We have expressed equations of lines in various forms. Among these are the equations

$$y = mx + b \qquad \text{and} \qquad \frac{x}{a} + \frac{y}{b} = 1.$$

Each of these equations has two constants which have geometrical significance. The constants of the first equation are m and b. When definite values are assigned to these letters, a line is completely determined. Other values for these, of course, determine other lines. Thus the quantities m and b are fixed for any particular line but change from line to line. These letters are called *parameters*. In the second equation a and b are the parameters.

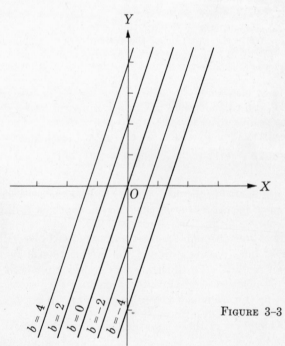

FIGURE 3–3

A linear equation with only one parameter is obtained if the other parameter is replaced by a fixed value. The resulting equation represents all lines with a particular property if the remaining parameter is allowed to vary. Each value assumed by the parameter yields an equation which represents a definite line. The collection of lines defined by a linear equation with one parameter is called a *family*, or *system*, of lines. For example, if $m = 3$, the point-slope equation becomes

$$y = 3x + b.$$

This equation represents the family of lines of slope 3, one line for each value of b. There are, of course, infinitely many lines in the family. In fact, a line of the family passes through each point of the coordinate plane. Figure 3–3 shows a few lines of the family corresponding to the indicated values of the parameter b.

EXAMPLE 1. Write the equation of the system of lines defined by each of the following conditions:
  (a) parallel to $3x - 2y = 5$,
  (b) passing through $(5, -2)$,
  (c) having the product of the intercepts equal to 4.

Solutions. The following equations are easily verified to be those required.
  (a) $3x - 2y = D$.   (b) $y + 2 = m(x - 5)$.

  (c) $\dfrac{x}{a} + \dfrac{y}{4/a} = 1$,   or $4x + a^2y = 4a$.

EXAMPLE 2. Write the equation of the system of lines which are parallel to $5x + 12y + 7 = 0$. Find the members of the family which are 3 units distant from the point $(2,1)$.

Solution. Each member of the family $5x + 12y + C = 0$ is parallel to the given line. We wish to find values of C which will yield lines 3 units from the point $(2,1)$, one passing above and the other below the point. Using the formula for the distance from a line to a point, we obtain the equations

$$\frac{5(2) + 12(1) + C}{13} = 3, \quad \frac{5(2) + 12(1) + C}{13} = -3.$$

The roots are $C = 17$ and $C = -61$. Hence the required equations are

$$5x + 12y + 17 = 0 \quad \text{and} \quad 5x + 12y - 61 = 0.$$

3–6 Family of lines through the intersection of two lines. The equation of the family of lines passing through the intersection of two given lines can be written readily. To illustrate, we consider the two intersecting lines

$$2x - 3y + 5 = 0, \quad 4x + y - 11 = 0.$$

From the left members of these equations we form the equation

$$(2x - 3y + 5) + k(4x + y - 11) = 0, \tag{1}$$

where k is a parameter. This equation is of the first degree in x and y for any value of k. Hence it represents a system of lines. Furthermore, each line of the family goes through the intersection of the given lines. We verify this statement by actual substitution. The given lines intersect at $(2,3)$. Then, using these values for x and y, we get

$$(4 - 9 + 5) + k(8 + 3 - 11) = 0,$$
$$0 + k(0) = 0,$$
$$0 = 0.$$

This result demonstrates that equation (1) is satisfied by the coordinates $(2,3)$ regardless of the value of k. Hence the equation defines a family of lines passing through the intersection of the given lines.

More generally, let the equations

$$A_1 x + B_1 y + C_1 = 0,$$
$$A_2 x + B_2 y + C_2 = 0$$

define two intersecting lines. Then the equation

$$(A_1 x + B_1 y + C_1) + k(A_2 x + B_2 y + C_2) = 0$$

represents a system of lines through the intersection of the given lines. To verify this statement, we first observe that the equation is linear for any value of k. Next we notice that the coordinates of the intersection point reduce each of the parts in parentheses to zero, and hence satisfy the equation for any value of k.

EXAMPLE. Write the equation of the system of lines through the intersection of $x - 7y + 3 = 0$ and $4x + 2y - 5 = 0$. Find the member of the family which has the slope 3.

Solution. The equation of the system of lines passing through the intersection of the given lines is

$$(x - 7y + 3) + k(4x + 2y - 5) = 0,$$

or, collecting terms,

$$(1 + 4k)x + (-7 + 2k)y + 3 - 5k = 0.$$

The slope of each member of this system, except for the vertical line, is $-\dfrac{1 + 4k}{2k - 7}$. Equating this fraction to the required slope gives

$$-\frac{1 + 4k}{2k - 7} = 3, \quad \text{and} \quad k = 2.$$

The member of the system for $k = 2$ is $9x - 3y - 7 = 0$.

EXERCISE 3–2

Find the distance from the line to the point in each problem 1–6.

1. $5x + 12y + 60 = 0$; $(3,2)$. 　　　　2. $4x - 3y = 15$; $(4,1)$.

3. $x + y - 3 = 0$; $(4,5)$.   4. $3x + y = 10$; $(-3,-1)$.

5. $-2x + 5y + 7 = 0$; $(6,0)$.   6. $y = 7$; $(3,-8)$.

Determine the distance between the pair of parallel lines in each problem 7–10.

7. $4x - 3y - 9 = 0$, $4x - 3y - 24 = 0$.

8. $12x + 5y = 13$, $12x + 5y = 104$.

9. $15x - 8y - 34 = 0$, $15x - 8y + 51 = 0$.

10. $x + y + 7 = 0$, $x + y - 11 = 0$.

Write the equation of the system of lines possessing the given property in each problem 11–18. In each case assign three values to the parameter and draw the corresponding lines.

11. Parallel to $7x - 4y = 3$.

12. Passing through $(-3,4)$.

13. Having the x-intercept twice the y-intercept.

14. Perpendicular to $2x - 5y + 3 = 0$.

15. Having the y-intercept equal to -4.

16. Having the sum of the intercepts equal to 10.

17. Through the intersection of $x - 2y + 7 = 0$ and $5x - 7y - 3 = 0$.

18. Forming with the coordinate axes a triangle of area 16.

Tell what geometric property is possessed by all the lines of each system in problems 19–26.

19. $y = mx + 4$.   20. $y = 2x + b$.

21. $9x + 2y = k$.   22. $y + 4 = m(x - 3)$.

23. $\dfrac{x}{a} + \dfrac{y}{3} = 1$.   24. $\dfrac{x}{a} + \dfrac{y}{4 + a} = 1$.

25. $(4x - 7y - 7) + ky = 0$.   26. $(4x + y + 1) + k(3x + 7y) = 0$.

27. In the preceding problems 19–26 determine the line of the system which passes through $(3,0)$.

28. Write the equation of the family of lines of slope -3, and find the two members passing 5 units from the origin.

In each problem 29–34 find the equation of the line which passes through the intersection of the pair of lines and satisfies the other given condition.

29. $3x + y - 2 = 0$, $x + 5y - 4 = 0$; through $(5,2)$.

30. $5x + 3y + 2 = 0$, $x - y - 2 = 0$; $m = -3$.

31. $x - 11y = 0$, $3x + y - 5 = 0$; a vertical line.

32. $6x - 2y = 3$, $x - 5y = 4$; $m = 0$.

33. $3x - 4y - 2 = 0$, $3x + 4y + 1 = 0$; intercepts are equal.

34. $2x - y - 5 = 0$, $x + y - 4 = 0$; passing through $(0,0)$.

35. The sides of a triangle are on the lines defined by $2x - 3y + 4 = 0$, $x + y + 3 = 0$, and $5x - 4y - 20 = 0$. Without solving for the vertices, find the equations of the altitudes.

36. Find the equations of the bisectors of the angles formed by the lines $4x + 3y - 12 = 0$ and $5x - 12y - 60 = 0$. [*Suggestion:* Let $P(x,y)$ be a point on a bisector and use the fact that each point of a bisector is equally distant from the sides.]

37. Find the equations of the bisectors of the angles formed by the lines $x + 2y + 3 = 0$ and $2x + y - 2 = 0$.

38. Write the equation $Ax + By + C = 0$ in normal form. Show that in this form the coefficient of x is equal to $\cos \omega$ and the coefficient of y is equal to $\sin \omega$, where ω is the inclination of the perpendicular segment drawn from the origin to the line.

CHAPTER 4

TRANSFORMATION OF COORDINATES

4–1 Introduction. Suppose that we have a curve in the coordinate plane and the equation which represents the curve. We wish to take another pair of axes in the plane and find the equation of the same curve with respect to the new axes. The new equation will depend on the original equation and the location of the new axes. The process of changing from one pair of axes to another is called a *transformation of coordinates*.

The device of transforming coordinates is a powerful and much used procedure. Numerous problems, many of a practical nature, can be conveniently begun with the coordinate axes in a certain position and carried forward more easily by using axes in another position. We shall find in Chapter 5 that considerable advantage is gained by the transformation process. There the study of second degree equations and their loci is greatly simplified by the proper location of the coordinate axes.

4–2 Translation of axes. When the new axes are parallel to the original axes, and similarly directed, the transformation is called a *translation of axes*. The coordinates of each point of the plane are changed under a translation of axes. Consequently, the equation of a curve referred to the original axes and the equation of the same curve referred to the new axes are, in general, not the same.

To see how the coordinates of a point are changed by a translation of axes, notice Fig. 4–1. The new axes $O'X'$ and $O'Y'$ are parallel respectively to the old axes OX and OY. The coordinates of the new origin O' referred to the original axes are denoted by (h,k). Thus the new axes can be obtained by shifting the old axes h units horizontally and k units vertically while keeping their directions unchanged. Let x and y stand for the coordinates of any point P when referred to the old axes and let x' and y' be the coordinates of the point P when referred to the new axes. It is evident from the figure that

$$x = ON = OM + O'Q = h + x',$$
$$y = NP = MO' + QP = k + y'.$$

Hence

$$x = x' + h, \quad y = y' + k. \tag{1}$$

These formulas give the relations of the old and new coordinates. They hold for all points of the plane, where the new origin O' is any chosen

45

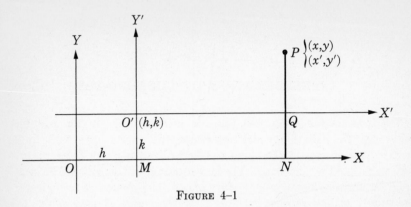

FIGURE 4–1

point of the plane. Holding for all points of the plane, the formulas apply in particular to the points of a curve. Consequently, the substitutions $x' + h$ for x, and $y' + k$ for y in the equation of a curve referred to the original axes yield the equation of the same curve referred to the translated axes.

EXAMPLE 1. Find the transformed equation of

$$xy - 3x + 2y - 12 = 0$$

if the origin is translated to the point $(-2,3)$.

Solution. Here $h = -2$ and $k = 3$. Hence the translation equations (1) are

$$x = x' - 2 \quad \text{and} \quad y = y' + 3.$$

Making these substitutions in the given equation, we get

$$(x' - 2)(y' + 3) - 3(x' - 2) + 2(y' + 3) - 12 = 0,$$
$$x'y' + 3x' - 2y' - 6 - 3x' + 6 + 2y' + 6 - 12 = 0,$$
$$x'y' - 6 = 0.$$

The transformed equation has no first degree terms. The graph is more easily constructed by use of this equation and the new axes. The origin of the new axes is 2 units to the left of the old origin and 3 units upward. Both sets of axes and the graph are drawn in Fig. 4–2.

EXAMPLE 2. Translate the axes so that the equation

$$2x^2 + 3y^2 - 10x + 18y + 26 = 0$$

is transformed to a simpler form.

Solution. We do not know in advance what the translation should be. Hence we use the translation formulas with h and k unknown. Thus we have

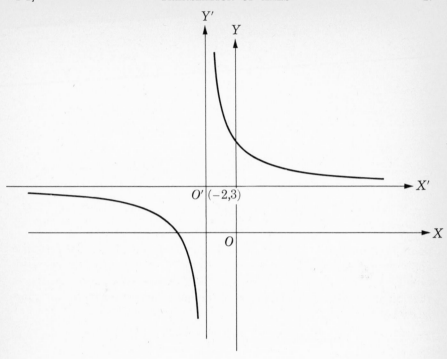

FIGURE 4–2

$$2(x' + h)^2 + 3(y' + k)^2 - 10(x' + h) + 18(y' + k) + 26 = 0,$$

$$2x'^2 + 3y'^2 + (4h - 10)x' + (6k + 18)y' + 2h^2 + 3k^2 - 10h + 18k + 26 = 0. \quad (2)$$

We set the coefficients of x' and y' equal to zero. This gives $4h - 10 = 0$ and $6k + 18 = 0$, and hence $h = 5/2$, $k = -3$. These values for h and k reduce equation (2) to

$$2x'^2 + 3y'^2 - (27/2) = 0, \quad \text{or} \quad 4x'^2 + 6y'^2 = 27.$$

This simplification can also be made by completing the squares in the x and y terms. Using this plan, we have from the original equation

$$2(x^2 - 5x \quad) + 3(y^2 + 6y \quad) = -26,$$

$$2[x^2 - 5x + (25/4)] + 3(y^2 + 6y + 9) = -26 + (25/2) + 27,$$

$$2[x - (5/2)]^2 + 3(y + 3)^2 = 27/2.$$

In this form we observe that the transformation equations $x = x' + 5/2$ and $y = y' - 3$ will yield an equation free of first degree terms. Thus we obtain, as before, $4x'^2 + 6y'^2 = 27$.

EXAMPLE 3. By a translation of axes, find a simplification of the equation

$$x^2 - 6x - 6y - 15 = 0.$$

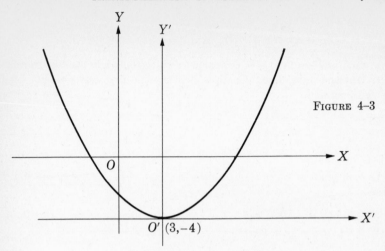

FIGURE 4–3

Solution. Applying the translation formulas, we have

$$(x' + h)^2 - 6(x' + h) - 6(y' + k) - 15 = 0,$$
$$x'^2 + 2hx' + h^2 - 6x' - 6h - 6y' - 6k - 15 = 0,$$
$$x'^2 + (2h - 6)x' - 6y' + (h^2 - 6h - 6k - 15) = 0.$$

The x'^2 and y' terms have coefficients independent of h and k, and may not be eliminated. We can achieve a simplification, however, by eliminating the x' term and the constant terms. Thus solving the equations

$$2h - 6 = 0 \quad \text{and} \quad h^2 - 6h - 6k - 15 = 0$$

simultaneously gives $h = 3$, $k = -4$. These values for h and k lead to the equation

$$x'^2 - 6y' = 0.$$

This result can also be obtained by completing the square in the x terms, and selecting the translation which will eliminate the x' term and the constant terms. Thus the given equation yields

$$x^2 - 6x + 9 = 6y + 15 + 9,$$
$$(x - 3)^2 = 6(y + 4).$$

By translating the origin to $(3, -4)$, this equation becomes $x'^2 = 6y'$. Both sets of axes and the graph are drawn in Fig. 4–3.

EXERCISE 4–1

Determine the new equation in each problem 1–8 if the origin is translated to the given point.

1. $3x + 2y = 6$; $(4, -3)$.   2. $5x - 4y + 3 = 0$; $(1, 2)$.

3. $(y - 2)^2 = 6(x - 3)$; $(2, 3)$.

4. $(x + 3)^2 + (y + 5)^2 = 25$; $(-3, -5)$.

5. $x^2 + y^2 + 12x - 8y + 48 = 0$; $(-6, 4)$.

6. $x^2 - 4x - 7y + 46 = 0$; $(2, 6)$.

7. $xy - x - y - 10 = 0$; $(1,1)$.

8. $x^3 - 3x^2 + 3x = y + 3$; $(1,-2)$.

In each problem 9–14 give the point to which the origin must be translated in order that the transformed equation shall have no first degree term. Find also the new equation.

9. $x^2 + y^2 - 2x - 4y - 4 = 0$.

10. $2x^2 + 2y^2 - 8x + 5 = 0$.

11. $xy - 2x - 3y - 8 = 0$.

12. $x^2 - y^2 - 8x + 6y + 3 = 0$.

13. $2x^2 + 4y^2 + 12x + 8y + 4 = 0$.

14. $9x^2 + 4y^2 - 8y = 0$.

In each problem 15–18 eliminate the constant term and one of the first degree terms.

15. $y^2 - 6y + 4x + 5 = 0$.

16. $x^2 - 2x - 8y - 15 = 0$.

17. $y^2 + 10x + 4y + 24 = 0$.

18. $y^2 - 4y - x + 1 = 0$.

4–3 Rotation of axes. When the new axes have the same origin but directions different from the original axes, the transformation is called a *rotation of axes*. That is, the new axes may be obtained by rotating the original axes through an angle about the origin.

We shall derive transformation formulas, for a rotation through an angle θ, which express the old coordinates in terms of the new coordinates. In Fig. 4–4 the coordinates of the point P are (x,y) referred to the original axes OX and OY, and are (x',y') when referred to the new axes OX' and OY'. We notice that $x = OM$ and $y = MP$, $x' = OS$ and $y' = SP$. The segment RS is drawn parallel to the x-axis and NS is parallel to the y-axis. Hence we have

$$x = OM = ON - MN = ON - RS = x' \cos \theta - y' \sin \theta,$$
$$y = MP = MR + RP = NS + RP = x' \sin \theta + y' \cos \theta.$$

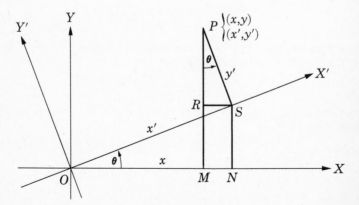

FIGURE 4–4

The rotation formulas, therefore, are

$$x = x' \cos \theta - y' \sin \theta,$$
$$y = x' \sin \theta + y' \cos \theta. \tag{1}$$

We have derived these formulas for the special case in which θ is an acute angle and the point P is in the first quadrant of both sets of axes. The formulas hold, however, for any θ and for all positions of P. A proof that the formulas hold generally could be made by observing the proper conventions as to the sign of θ and the signs of all distances involved.

EXAMPLE 1. Transform the equation $x^2 - y^2 - 9 = 0$ by rotating the axes through 45°.

Solution. Using $\theta = 45°$, the rotation formulas (1) are

$$x = \frac{x'}{\sqrt{2}} - \frac{y'}{\sqrt{2}}, \quad y = \frac{x'}{\sqrt{2}} + \frac{y'}{\sqrt{2}}.$$

We make the substitutions in the given equation and have

$$\left(\frac{x'}{\sqrt{2}} - \frac{y'}{\sqrt{2}} \right)^2 - \left(\frac{x'}{\sqrt{2}} + \frac{y'}{\sqrt{2}} \right)^2 - 9 = 0,$$

$$\frac{x'^2}{2} - x'y' + \frac{y'^2}{2} - \frac{x'^2}{2} - x'y' - \frac{y'^2}{2} - 9 = 0,$$

$$2x'y' + 9 = 0.$$

The graph and both sets of axes are constructed in Fig. 4–5.

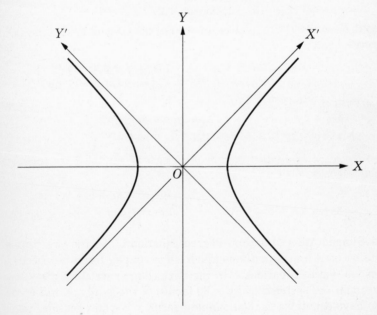

FIGURE 4–5

EXAMPLE 2. Find the acute angle of rotation such that the transformed equation of $2x^2 + \sqrt{3}xy + y^2 = 8$ will have no $x'y'$ term.

Solution. We employ the rotation formulas in order to find the required angle θ. Substituting for x and y, we get

$$2(x' \cos \theta - y' \sin \theta)^2 + \sqrt{3}(x' \cos \theta - y' \sin \theta)(x' \sin \theta + y' \cos \theta)$$
$$+ (x' \sin \theta + y' \cos \theta)^2 = 8.$$

We perform the indicated multiplications, collect like terms, and obtain

$$(2 \cos^2 \theta + \sqrt{3} \sin \theta \cos \theta + \sin^2 \theta)x'^2 + (-2 \sin \theta \cos \theta + \sqrt{3} \cos^2 \theta$$
$$- \sqrt{3} \sin^2 \theta)x'y' + (2 \sin^2 \theta - \sqrt{3} \sin \theta \cos \theta + \cos^2 \theta)y'^2 = 8. \quad (2)$$

Since the $x'y'$ term is to vanish, we set its coefficient equal to zero. Thus we have

$$-2 \sin \theta \cos \theta + \sqrt{3}(\cos^2 \theta - \sin^2 \theta) = 0.$$

Using the identities $\sin 2\theta = 2 \sin \theta \cos \theta$ and $\cos 2\theta = \cos^2 \theta - \sin^2 \theta$, the equation takes the form

$$-\sin 2\theta + \sqrt{3} \cos 2\theta = 0,$$

whence

$$\tan 2\theta = \sqrt{3}, \quad 2\theta = 60°, \quad \theta = 30°.$$

A rotation of 30° eliminates the $x'y'$ term. This value of θ reduces equation (2) to

$$5x'^2 + y'^2 = 16.$$

EXERCISE 4–2

Find the new equation in problems 1–8 when the axes are rotated through the given angle.

1. $\sqrt{3}x - y = 4; \theta = 60°$.   2. $x + y = 6; \theta = 45°$.
3. $xy = 4; \theta = 45°$.   4. $x^2 + y^2 = a^2; \theta = 40°$.
5. $x^2 + xy + y^2 = 1; \theta = 45°$.   6. $x^2 - \sqrt{3}xy + 2y^2 = 2; \theta = 30°$.
7. $x^2 - 4xy + 4y^2 - 8\sqrt{5}x - 4\sqrt{5}y = 0; \theta = \arctan \frac{1}{2}$.
8. $x^2 + \sqrt{3}xy + 2y^2 = 3; \theta = \arctan \sqrt{3}$.

Find the angle of rotation in each problem 9–12 such that the transformed equation will have no $x'y'$ term.

9. $3xy + y - 2 = 0$.   10. $x^2 - xy + 5 = 0$.
11. $x^2 - 3xy + 4y^2 + 7 = 0$.   12. $x^2 + 3xy - x + y = 0$.

4–4 Simplification of second degree equations. In the two preceding sections we used transformations which led to simpler forms of various first and second degree equations. In the next chapter we shall study second degree equations systematically. To facilitate this study, it will be desirable to have equations in their simplest forms. We now consider the simplest forms of second degree equations.

The general second degree, or quadratic, equation in x and y is represented by

$$Ax^2 + Bxy + Cy^2 + Dx + Ey + F = 0. \tag{1}$$

At least one of the constants A, B, and C must be different from zero in order for the equation to be of the second degree. We assume, too, that not all the coefficients of terms involving one of the variables is zero. That is, both x and y appear in the equation.

If $B = 0$, and A and C are both different from zero, we may complete the squares in the x and y terms, as in Example 2, Section 4–2. Then it is easy to find the translation which will reduce the equation to the form

$$A'x'^2 + C'y'^2 + F' = 0.$$

If $B = 0$ and one of the coefficients A and C is also zero, we may find the translation, as in Example 3, Section 4–2, which will reduce the equation (1) to one of the forms

$$B'y'^2 + D'x' = 0 \qquad \text{or} \qquad A'x'^2 + E'y' = 0.$$

If $B \neq 0$, an essential part of the simplification consists in obtaining a transformed equation lacking the product term $x'y'$. We shall show how to determine immediately an angle of rotation which will serve for this purpose. In equation (1) we substitute the right members of the rotation formulas for x and y. This gives, after collecting like terms, the equation

$$A'x'^2 + B'x'y' + C'y'^2 + D'x' + E'y' + F' = 0,$$

where the new coefficients are

$$A' = A \cos^2 \theta + B \sin \theta \cos \theta + C \sin^2 \theta,$$
$$B' = B \cos 2\theta - (A - C) \sin 2\theta,$$
$$C' = A \sin^2 \theta - B \sin \theta \cos \theta + C \cos^2 \theta,$$
$$D' = D \cos \theta + E \sin \theta,$$
$$E' = E \cos \theta - D \sin \theta,$$
$$F' = F.$$

The $x'y'$ term will vanish only if its coefficient is zero. Hence θ must satisfy the equation

$$B' = B \cos 2\theta - (A - C) \sin 2\theta = 0.$$

If $A \neq C$, the solution is

$$\tan 2\theta = \frac{B}{A - C}.$$

This formula yields the angle of rotation except when $A = C$. If $A = C$, the coefficient of $x'y'$ is $B \cos 2\theta$. Then the term vanishes by giving θ the value 45°. Thus we see that an equation of the form (1) with an xy term can be transformed into an equation free of the product term $x'y'$.

We summarize the preceding results in the following theorem.

THEOREM.   *A second degree equation*

$$Ax^2 + Bxy + Cy^2 + Dx + Ey + F = 0$$

in which $B = 0$ can be transformed by a translation into one of the forms

$$A'x'^2 + C'y'^2 + F = 0,$$
$$A'x'^2 + E'y' = 0, \tag{2}$$
$$C'y'^2 + D'x' = 0.$$

If $B \neq 0$, one of these forms can be obtained by a rotation and a translation (if necessary).   The angle of rotation θ (chosen acute) is obtained from the equation

$$\tan 2\theta = \frac{B}{A - C}, \quad \text{if} \quad A \neq C,$$

or

$$\theta = 45°, \quad \text{if} \quad A = C.$$

By this theorem we see how to find the value of $\tan 2\theta$.   The rotation formulas, however, contain $\sin \theta$ and $\cos \theta$.   These functions can be obtained from the trigonometric identities

$$\sin \theta = \sqrt{\frac{1 - \cos 2\theta}{2}}, \quad \cos \theta = \sqrt{\frac{1 + \cos 2\theta}{2}}.$$

The positive sign is selected before each radical because we shall restrict θ to an acute angle.

EXAMPLE.   Reduce the equation

$$73x^2 - 72xy + 52y^2 + 100x - 200y + 100 = 0$$

to one of the forms (2).

Solution.   We first transform the equation so that the product term $x'y'$ will be lacking.   To find the angle of rotation, we have

$$\tan 2\theta = \frac{B}{A - C} = \frac{-72}{73 - 52} = \frac{-24}{7},$$

whence

$$\cos 2\theta = \frac{-7}{25}.$$

Hence

$$\sin \theta = \sqrt{\frac{1 - \cos 2\theta}{2}} = \frac{4}{5} \quad \text{and} \quad \cos \theta = \sqrt{\frac{1 + \cos 2\theta}{2}} = \frac{3}{5}.$$

The rotation formulas are then

$$x = \frac{3x' - 4y'}{5} \quad \text{and} \quad y = \frac{4x' + 3y'}{5}.$$

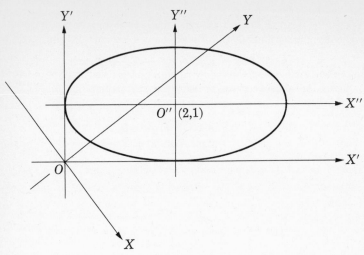

FIGURE 4–6

By substituting for x and y in the given equation and simplifying, we get

$$x'^2 + 4y'^2 - 4x' - 8y' + 4 = 0.$$

Completing the squares in the x' and y' terms, this equation becomes

$$(x' - 2)^2 + 4(y' - 1)^2 - 4 = 0.$$

Finally, a translation to the point $(2,1)$ yields the desired form

$$x''^2 + 4y''^2 - 4 = 0.$$

It is much easier to draw the graph from this equation than by using the original equation. The graph and the three sets of axes are constructed in Fig. 4–6.

EXERCISE 4–3

Translate the axes so that the constant term is eliminated. Draw both sets of axes and the graph:

    1. $3x - 4y = 6.$ 2. $x = 6.$

Rotate the axes through an acute angle such that the x' or the y' term is eliminated:

    3. $3x - 4y = 6.$ 4. $x + y = 0.$

Reduce each of the equations 5–8 to one of the simplified forms (2).

    5. $x^2 - 2xy + y^2 - 8\sqrt{2}y - 8 = 0.$
    6. $3x^2 + 2\sqrt{3}xy + y^2 - 2x - 2\sqrt{3}y - 16 = 0.$
    7. $73x^2 - 72xy + 52y^2 + 380x - 160y + 400 = 0.$
    8. $7x^2 + 48xy - 7y^2 - 150x - 50y + 100 = 0.$

9. Show that the graph of the quadratic equation in one variable $Ax^2 + Dx + F = 0$ is one line, two parallel lines, or that no real value of x satisfies the equation, according as the discriminant $D^2 - 4AF$ is zero, positive, or negative.

Write the left members of the following equations as the product of two linear factors. Draw the graphs corresponding to the real factors.

10. $x^2 - x - 6 = 0$.   11. $x^2 + 6x + 9 = 0$.

12. $x^2 + x - 1 = 0$.   13. $x^2 + x + 1 = 0$.

14. Work out all the steps of the rotation transformation which is applied to equation (1), Section 4-4.

CHAPTER 5

THE SECOND DEGREE EQUATION

5–1 Introduction. In this chapter we shall study second degree, or quadratic, equations in two variables. The general quadratic equation in x and y may be expressed in the form

$$Ax^2 + Bxy + Cy^2 + Dx + Ey + F = 0. \tag{1}$$

The study of this kind of equation in some respects is less simple than the case of the linear equation. Any linear equation in two variables has a locus, and the locus is a straight line. In contrast, not all second degree equations have loci, and those having loci represent different types of curves. Our principal interest, however, will be in equations which have loci.

The locus of a quadratic equation in two variables is called a *conic section* or, more simply, a *conic*. This designation comes from the fact that the locus or curve can be obtained as the intersection of a right circular cone and a plane.* Conic sections were investigated, particularly by Greek mathematicians, long before analytic methods were introduced. Various properties of conics were discovered and this phase of geometry received much emphasis. Today the interest in conic sections is enhanced by numerous important theoretical and practical applications which have been found.

Obviously, different kinds of conic sections are possible. A plane, not passing through the vertex of a cone, may cut all the elements of one nappe and make a closed curve (Fig. 5–1). If the plane is parallel to an element, the intersection extends indefinitely far along one nappe but does not cut the other. The plane may cut both nappes and make a section of two parts, with each extending indefinitely far along a nappe. In addition to these sections the plane may pass through the vertex of the cone and determine a point, a line, or two intersecting lines. An intersection of this kind is sometimes called a *degenerate* conic. The section consisting of two intersecting lines approaches two parallel lines if the cone is made to approach a cylinder by letting the vertex recede indefinitely far. For this reason, two parallel lines are classed with the degenerate conics.

---

* A right circular cone is the surface generated by a line which passes through a fixed point on a fixed line and moves so that it makes a constant angle with the fixed line. The fixed point is the vertex and the generating line in any position is called an element. The vertex separates the cone into two parts called *nappes*.

56

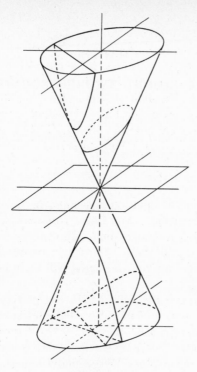

FIGURE 5–1

5–2 The simplified equations of conics. Despite the interesting geo-metric way in which conics first became known, we shall approach their study as loci of second degree equations rather than as the intersections of planes and cones. In our study we shall take advantage of the simpli-fied equations

$$Ax^2 + Cy^2 + F = 0, \tag{2}$$

$$Cy^2 + Dx = 0, \tag{3}$$

$$Ax^2 + Ey = 0, \tag{4}$$

which were obtained in Section 4–4.

Normally, equations (2)–(4) represent conics. There are exceptional cases, however, depending on the values of the coefficients. The excep-tional cases are not our main interest, but we do notice them. Equa-tion (2) has no locus if A, C, and F are all of the same sign, for then there are no real values of x and y for which the terms of the left member add to zero. If $F = 0$, and A and C have the same sign, only the coordinates of the origin satisfy the equation. Selections of values for the coefficients may be variously made so that equation (2) represents two intersecting lines, two parallel lines, or one line. An equation of the form (3) or (4) always has a locus, but the locus is a line if the coefficient of the first degree term is zero. The point and line loci of second degree equations are called *degenerate* conics, as was previously noted.

Aside from the exceptional cases, we shall discover that equations of the form (2) represent different types of curves, depending on the relative values of A and C. We shall consider the cases in which (a) $A = C$, (b) A and C have the same sign but are unequal, and (c) A and C have opposite signs. The equations (3) and (4) are not essentially different so far as their loci are concerned. This statement may be justified by noting that a rotation of 90° will transform either equation into one having the form of the other.

5–3 The parabola. We shall consider first equations (3) and (4). Each of these equations has only one second degree term, and in this respect is simpler than equation (2). By division and transposition we reduce the equations to the forms

$$y^2 = 4ax, \tag{5}$$

$$x^2 = 4ay, \tag{6}$$

which will be found more convenient. The locus of an equation of either of these forms, or which can be reduced to one of these forms, is called a *parabola*. Restricting our attention for the moment to equation (5), we observe at once certain characteristics of its locus. The graph passes through the origin and is symmetric with respect to the x-axis. If $a > 0$, x may have any positive value or zero, but may have no negative value. As x increases, the values of y increase numerically. Hence the graph

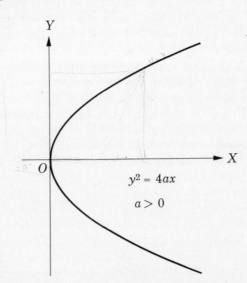

$$y^2 = 4ax$$

$$a > 0$$

FIGURE 5–2

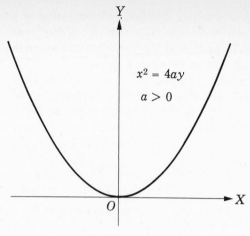

$$x^2 = 4ay$$
$$a > 0$$

FIGURE 5–3

extends indefinitely far into the first and fourth quadrants (Fig. 5–2). If $a < 0$, then x may assume only zero and negative values, and the graph extends into the second and third quadrants.

Similarly, the graph of equation (6) passes through the origin and is symmetric with respect to the y-axis. The parabola opens upward or downward depending on whether a is positive or negative.

The line of symmetry of a parabola is called the *axis* of the parabola. The intersection of the axis and the parabola is called the *vertex*.

5–4 The focus-directrix property of a parabola. Having observed certain obvious properties of a parabola, we look more closely for further information.   We see that the left member of $y^2 = 4ax$ represents the square of a distance, and the right member is a constant times the first power of a distance.   Keeping distances in mind, we inquire if the equation may be altered so that both sides represent like powers of distances.   The right member may be regarded as the middle term of the square of a binomial, and it becomes a perfect square by the addition of $x^2 + 4a^2$.   This changes the left side to $x^2 + 4a^2 + y^2$, which is not a perfect square.   The left side now appears to need a first degree term in x.   With this suggestion, we return to the original equation and introduce a first degree term in the left member by transposing from the right member.   Thus we have

$$y^2 - 2ax = 2ax,$$
$$x^2 - 2ax + a^2 + y^2 = x^2 + 2ax + a^2,$$
$$(x - a)^2 + y^2 = (x + a)^2.$$

Taking positive square roots, we obtain

$$\sqrt{(x - a)^2 + y^2} = \pm(x + a),$$

where the sign in the right member is to be chosen so that $(x + a)$ is positive. This equation is subject to a ready interpretation in terms of distances. The left member is the distance between any point (x,y) of the parabola and the point $F(a,0)$. The right member is the distance from the line $x = -a$ to the point (x,y). Hence we conclude that all points of a parabola are equally distant from a fixed point and a fixed line. The fixed point is named the *focus* and the fixed line the *directrix*. We state this result as a theorem.

THEOREM. *Each point of a parabola is equally distant from a fixed point (focus) and a fixed line (directrix).*

The focus of $y^2 = 4ax$ is $F(a,0)$ and the directrix is the line $x = -a$.

The focus of $x^2 = 4ay$ is $F(0,a)$ and the directrix is the line $y = -a$.

The chord drawn through the focus and perpendicular to the axis of a parabola is given the Latin name *latus rectum*. The length of the latus rectum can be determined from the coordinates of its end points. By substituting a for x in the equation $y^2 = 4ax$, we find

$$y^2 = 4a^2 \quad \text{and} \quad y = \pm 2a.$$

Hence the end points of the latus rectum are $(a,-2a)$ and $(a,2a)$. This makes the length equal to the numerical value of $4a$.

The vertex and the extremities of the latus rectum are sufficient for making a rough sketch of the parabola. A few additional points, however,

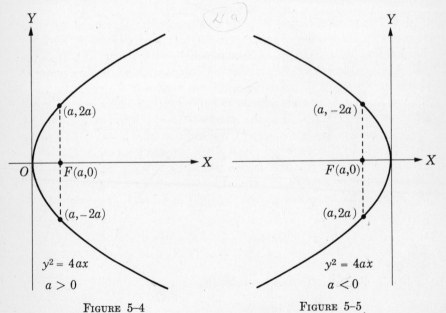

FIGURE 5-4   FIGURE 5-5

would greatly improve the accuracy. Figures 5–4 to 5–7 show carefully constructed parabolas corresponding to the equations $y^2 = 4ax$ and $x^2 = 4ay$.

Summarizing, we make the following remarks regarding the equations

$$y^2 = 4ax, \tag{5}$$

$$x^2 = 4ay. \tag{6}$$

Equation (5) represents a parabola with vertex at the origin and focus at $(a,0)$. The parabola opens to the right if a is positive and to the left if a is negative. Equation (6) represents a parabola with vertex at the origin and focus at $(0,a)$. The parabola opens upward if a is positive and downward if a is negative. The numerical value of a is the distance

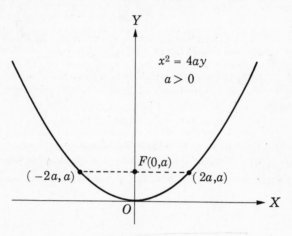

FIGURE 5–6

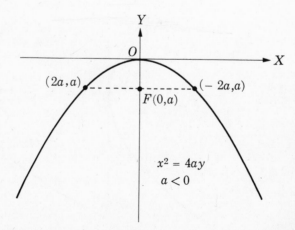

FIGURE 5–7

between the vertex and the focus, and its sign tells in which direction to measure this distance. The length of the latus rectum is equal to the absolute value of $4a$. The graph of an equation in one of these forms can be quickly drawn, the vertex and ends of the latus rectum being sufficient for a rough sketch.

The forms (5) and (6) can be applied to find the equations of parabolas which satisfy certain specified conditions. We illustrate their use in some examples.

EXAMPLE 1. Write the equation of the parabola with vertex at the origin and the focus at (0,4).

Solution. Equation (6) applies here. The distance from the vertex to the focus is 4, and hence $a = 4$. Substituting this value for a, we get

$$x^2 = 16y.$$

EXAMPLE 2. A parabola has its vertex at the origin, its axis along the x-axis, and passes through the point $(-3,6)$. Find its equation.

Solution. The equation of the parabola is of the form $y^2 = 4ax$. To determine the value of a, we substitute the coordinates of the given point in this equation. Thus we obtain

$$36 = 4a(-3), \quad \text{and} \quad 4a = -12.$$

The required equation is $y^2 = -12x$. The focus is at $(-3,0)$, and the given point is the upper end of the latus rectum. The graph is constructed in Fig. 5–8.

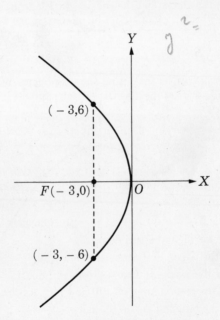

FIGURE 5–8

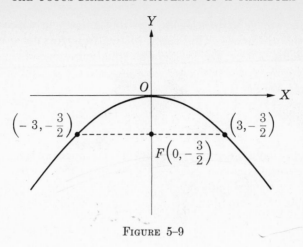

FIGURE 5–9

EXAMPLE 3. The equation of a parabola is $x^2 = -6y$. Find the coordinates of the focus, the equation of the directrix, and the length of the latus rectum.

Solution. The equation is of the form (6), where a is negative. Hence the focus is on the negative y-axis and the parabola opens downward. From the equation $4a = -6$, we find $a = -3/2$. Therefore the coordinates of the focus are $(0,-3/2)$ and the directrix is $y = 3/2$. The length of the latus rectum is numerically equal to $4a$, and in this case is 6. The latus rectum extends 3 units to the left and 3 units to the right of the focus. The graph may be sketched by drawing through the vertex and the ends of the latus rectum. For more accurate graphing a few additional points could be plotted. (See Fig. 5–9.)

EXERCISE 5–1

Find the coordinates of the focus, the coordinates of the ends of the latus rectum, and the equation of the directrix of each parabola in problems 1–6. Sketch each curve.

1. $y^2 = 4x$.   2. $y^2 = -16x$.   3. $x^2 = -10y$.

4. $x^2 = 12y$.   5. $y^2 + 3x = 0$.   6. $x^2 - 8y = 0$.

Write the equation of the parabola with vertex at the origin and which satisfies the given conditions in each problem 7–16.

7. Focus at $(3,0)$.   8. Focus at $(-4,0)$.

9. Directrix is $x + 6 = 0$.   10. Directrix is $y - 4 = 0$.

11. Latus rectum 12, and opens downward.

12. Focus on the y-axis, and passes through $(2,8)$.

13. Axis along the y-axis, and passes through $(4,-3)$.

14. Ends of latus rectum are $(-3,-6)$ and $(-3,6)$.

15. Opens to the left, and passes through $(-1,-1)$.

16. Opens to the right, and the length of the latus rectum is 16.

17. A cable suspended from supports which are at the same height and 400 feet apart has a sag of 100 feet. If the cable hangs in the form of a parabola, find its equation, taking the origin at the lowest point.

18. Find the width of the cable of problem 17 at a height 50 feet above the lowest point.

5–5 The ellipse.

We next consider the equation

$$Ax^2 + Cy^2 + F = 0, \qquad (2)$$

where A and C have the same sign and F has the opposite sign. If $A = C$, we may write the equation as $x^2 + y^2 = -F/A$. The left member is the square of the distance of any point (x,y) from the origin. Hence the locus is a circle and the right member is the square of the radius. Indicating the radius by r, we have the more suggestive form

$$x^2 + y^2 = r^2. \qquad (7)$$

If $A \neq C$, the locus of equation (2), or an equation reducible to this form, is defined as an *ellipse*. By setting x and y in turn equal to zero, we find the squares of the intercepts on the axes to be $-F/A$ and $-F/C$. Using $a^2 = -F/A$ and $b^2 = -F/C$, equation (2) becomes

$$\frac{x^2}{a^2} + \frac{y^2}{b^2} = 1. \qquad (8)$$

The intercepts are thus brought into prominence, and for still other reasons this form will be convenient. We shall regard a and b as positive, and for definiteness take $a > b$.

We notice first that the graph of equation (8) is symmetric with respect to both coordinate axes. Solving for x and y in turn, we have

$$x = \pm \frac{a}{b} \sqrt{b^2 - y^2} \qquad \text{and} \qquad y = \pm \frac{b}{a} \sqrt{a^2 - x^2}.$$

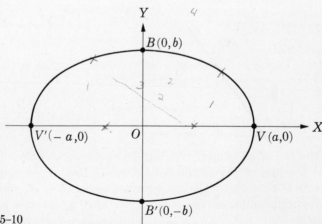

FIGURE 5–10

These equations show that y^2 must not exceed b^2, and x^2 must not exceed a^2. In other words, the permissible values of the variables are given by $-a \leq x \leq a$ and $-b \leq y \leq b$. The graph (Fig. 5–10) cuts the x-axis at the points $V'(-a,0)$ and $V(a,0)$, and cuts the y-axis at $B'(0,-b)$ and $B(0,b)$. The segment $V'V(= 2a)$ is called the *major axis* of the ellipse, and $B'B(= 2b)$ is the *minor axis*. The ends of the major axis are called *vertices*. The intersection of the major and minor axes is the *center* of the ellipse. (The designation of the vertices by V' and V comes from the first letter in the word vertex.)

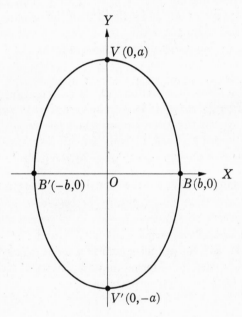

FIGURE 5–11

The graph of

$$\frac{y^2}{a^2} + \frac{x^2}{b^2} = 1 \tag{9}$$

is drawn in Fig. 5–11. The ellipses represented by equations (8) and (9) are alike except for their positions relative to the coordinate axes.

5–6 The foci of an ellipse. An important property of the ellipse is the fact that the sum of the distances from each point of the ellipse to two fixed points is constant. The fixed points, called *foci*, are on the major axis and equidistant from the center. We shall prove this property of the ellipse.

Figure 5–12 shows the graph of equation (8). The points $F'(-c,0)$ and $F(c,0)$ denote the foci, where for the moment c is undetermined. For the vertex V we have $F'V + FV = F'V + V'F' = 2a$. Thus the constant $2a$ is the sum of the distances from the vertex to the foci. Hence we need to show that the sum of the distances from any point on the ellipse to the foci is equal to $2a$. By considering next the special point B, the value of c may be determined. In order that $F'B + FB$ should be equal to $2a$, each of these segments must have a length equal to a. This gives, from the right triangle OFB, the relation $c^2 = a^2 - b^2.$ Using this relation and the equation of the ellipse, we next show that $F'P + FP$ is equal to $2a$, where $P(x,y)$ is any point of the ellipse. Denoting this sum by S, we have

$$S = \sqrt{(x+c)^2 + y^2} + \sqrt{(x-c)^2 + y^2}. \tag{a}$$

Whence, squaring and collecting like terms,

$$S^2 = 2x^2 + 2y^2 + 2c^2 + 2\sqrt{x^4 - 2c^2x^2 + c^4 + 2x^2y^2 + 2c^2y^2 + y^4}. \tag{b}$$

If we replace c^2 by $a^2 - b^2$, the radicand becomes

$$a^4 + b^4 + x^4 + y^4 - 2a^2b^2 - 2a^2x^2 + 2a^2y^2 + 2b^2x^2 - 2b^2y^2 + 2x^2y^2.$$

An examination of this expression reveals that it is equal to

$$(a^2 + b^2 - x^2 - y^2)^2$$

if the signs of each of the terms $-2a^2b^2$, $2a^2y^2$, and $2b^2x^2$ are reversed. The equation of the ellipse, (8), yields $2b^2x^2 + 2a^2y^2 - 2a^2b^2 = 0$, which shows that the signs of the three terms may be reversed without changing the value of the radicand. Hence we have

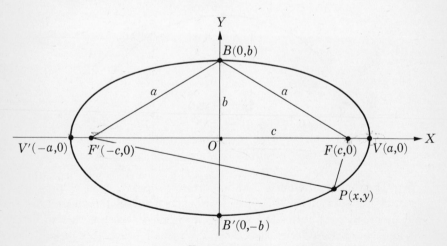

FIGURE 5–12

$$S^2 = 2x^2 + 2y^2 + 2a^2 - 2b^2 + 2(a^2 + b^2 - x^2 - y^2) = 4a^2$$

and

$$S = 2a.$$

We chose the positive square root of the radical of equation (b). This is necessary because the radical is the product of the two positive radicals of equation (a). That we chose the positive square root may be observed from the figure. We notice that $a^2 + b^2 > x^2 + y^2$, and hence $a^2 + b^2 - x^2 - y^2 > 0$. It is necessary also to select the positive square root of $4a^2$, since S is the sum of two positive quantities. We state the result as a theorem.

THEOREM. *The sum of the distances from each point of an ellipse to two fixed points (foci) of the major axis is constant and equal to the length of the major axis.*

The foci of $\dfrac{x^2}{a^2} + \dfrac{y^2}{b^2} = 1$ are the points $(-c,0)$ and $(c,0)$, where $c^2 = a^2 - b^2$.

The foci of $\dfrac{y^2}{a^2} + \dfrac{x^2}{b^2} = 1$ are the points $(0,-c)$ and $(0,c)$, where still $c^2 = a^2 - b^2$.

The chord through a focus and perpendicular to the major axis is called a *latus rectum*. Substituting $x = c$ in the equation of the ellipse (8) and using the relation $c^2 = a^2 - b^2$, the points $(c,-b^2/a)$ and $(c,b^2/a)$ are found to be the ends of one latus rectum. Hence the length of the latus rectum is $2b^2/a$. The ellipse and each latus rectum are drawn in Fig. 5–13.

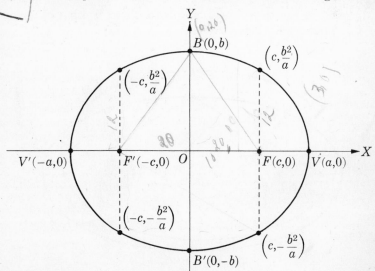

FIGURE 5–13

5-7 The eccentricity of an ellipse. The ratio c/a is called the *eccentricity* e of the ellipse. The shape of the ellipse depends on the value of its eccentricity. For example, suppose that we visualize an ellipse in which the major axis remains constant, while e starts at zero and approaches unity. If $e = 0$, the equations $e = c/a$ and $b^2 = a^2 - c^2$ show that $c = 0$ and $a = b$. The two foci are then coincident at the origin and the ellipse is a circle. As e increases, the foci separate, each receding from the origin, and b decreases. As e approaches 1, c approaches a, and b approaches 0. Thus the ellipse, starting as a circle, becomes narrow, with all its points near the major axis.

EXAMPLE 1. Find the equation of the ellipse with foci at $(0,\pm4)$ and a vertex (at 0,6.)

Solution. The location of the foci shows that the center of the ellipse is at the origin, that the equation is of the form (9), and that $c = 4$. The given vertex, 6 units from the center, makes $a = 6$. Using the relation $b^2 = a^2 - c^2$, we find $b^2 = 20$. Hence the required equation is

$$\frac{y^2}{36} + \frac{x^2}{20} = 1.$$

EXAMPLE 2. Sketch the ellipse $9x^2 + 25y^2 = 225$.

Solution. Dividing by 225 gives the form

$$\frac{x^2}{25} + \frac{y^2}{9} = 1.$$

Since the denominator of x^2 is greater than the denominator of y^2, the major axis

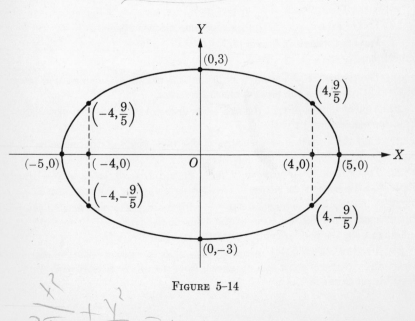

FIGURE 5-14

is along the x-axis. We see also that $a^2 = 25$, $b^2 = 9$, and $c = \sqrt{a^2 - b^2} = 4$. Hence the vertices are at $(\pm 5, 0)$, the ends of the minor axis at $(0, \pm 3)$, and the foci at $(\pm 4, 0)$. The length of a latus rectum is $2b^2/a = 18/5$. The locations of the ends of the axes and the ends of each latus rectum are sufficient for making a sketch of the ellipse. Figure 5–14 shows the curve with several important points indicated.

Exercise 5–2

Find the coordinates of the foci, the ends of the axes, and the ends of each latus rectum in problems 1–10. From this information sketch the curves.

1. $\dfrac{y^2}{25} + \dfrac{x^2}{9} = 1$.

2. $\dfrac{x^2}{169} + \dfrac{y^2}{25} = 1$.

3. $\dfrac{x^2}{169} + \dfrac{y^2}{144} = 1$.

4. $\dfrac{y^2}{25} + \dfrac{x^2}{16} = 1$.

5. $\dfrac{x^2}{49} + \dfrac{y^2}{25} = 1$.

6. $\dfrac{x^2}{9} + \dfrac{y^2}{4} = 1$.

7. $25x^2 + 4y^2 = 100$.

8. $x^2 + 4y^2 = 9$.

9. $4x^2 + y^2 = 4$.

10. $2x^2 + 3y^2 = 12$.

Write the equations of the ellipses whose axes coincide with the coordinate axes, and which satisfy the conditions given in problems 11–18.

11. Vertex $(4,0)$; end of minor axis $(0,3)$.

12. Focus $(2,0)$; vertex $(5,0)$.

13. Focus $(0,-4)$; minor axis 4.

14. Minor axis 12; vertex $(9,0)$.

15. Focus $(3,0)$; length of latus rectum 9.

16. End of minor axis $(5,0)$; length of latus rectum $\frac{50}{13}$.

17. Passing through $(3,5)$ and $(7,5/3)$.

18. Passing through $(3,\sqrt{2})$ and $(\sqrt{6},2)$.

19. The perimeter of a triangle is 30, and the points $(0,-5)$ and $(0,5)$ are two of the vertices. Find the locus of the third vertex.

20. A point moves so that the sum of its distances from $(-3,0)$ and $(3,0)$ is 8. Find the equation of its path.

21. Find the equation of the locus of the mid-points of the ordinates of the circle $x^2 + y^2 = 36$.

22. The ordinates of a curve are k times the ordinates of the circle $x^2 + y^2 = a^2$. Show that the curve is an ellipse if k is a positive number different from 1.

23. A line segment of length 12 moves with its ends always touching the coordinate axes. Find the equation of the locus of the point on the segment which is 4 units from the end, in contact with the x-axis.

24. A rod of length $a + b$ moves with its ends in contact with the coordinate axes. Show that the point at a distance a from the end in contact with the x-axis describes an ellipse if $a \neq b$.

25. The earth's orbit is an ellipse with the sun at one focus. The length of the major axis is 186,000,000 miles and the eccentricity is 0.0167. Find the distances from the ends of the major axis to the sun. These are the greatest and least distances from the earth to the sun.

5–8 The hyperbola. We return to the equation

$$Ax^2 + Cy^2 + F = 0$$

and now specify that A and C are to be of unlike signs. The graph for this case is called a *hyperbola*. If F has the same sign as C, the equation may be written in a more convenient form for study:

$$\frac{x^2}{a^2} - \frac{y^2}{b^2} = 1. \tag{10}$$

We regard a and b as positive but make no restriction as to their comparative values.

The graph of equation (10) is symmetric with respect to the coordinate axes. The permissible values for x and y become evident when each is expressed in terms of the other. Thus we get

$$x = \pm \frac{a}{b} \sqrt{b^2 + y^2} \qquad \text{and} \qquad y = \pm \frac{b}{a} \sqrt{x^2 - a^2}.$$

We see from the first of these equations that y may have any real value, and from the second that x may have any real value except those for which $x^2 < a^2$. Hence the hyperbola extends indefinitely far from the axes in each quadrant. But there is no part of the graph between the lines $x = -a$ and $x = a$. This means that the hyperbola consists of two separate parts, or *branches* (Fig. 5–15). The x-intercept points are $V'(-a,0)$ and $V(a,0)$, and are called *vertices*. The segment $V'V$ is the *transverse axis*. There is no y-intercept, but the segment from $B'(0,-b)$ to $B(0,b)$ is called the *conjugate axis*. While the conjugate axis has no point in common with the hyperbola, it has an important relation to the curve, as we shall see. The intersection of the axes is called the *center*.

The hyperbola has associated with it two fixed points called the *foci*. The foci of the hyperbola defined by equation (10) are $F'(-c,0)$ and $F(c,0)$, where $c^2 = a^2 + b^2$. The difference of the distances from each point of the hyperbola to the foci is a constant. The proof of this property of the hyperbola may be made almost exactly as in the case of the ellipse, and is left for the reader.

The chord through a focus and perpendicular to the transverse axis is called a *latus rectum*. By substituting $x = c$ in equation (10) and using the relation $c^2 = a^2 + b^2$, the points $(c,-b^2/a)$ and $(c,b^2/a)$ are found to be the extremities of a latus rectum. Hence its length is $2b^2/a$.

It is important to note that the relation among the three quantities

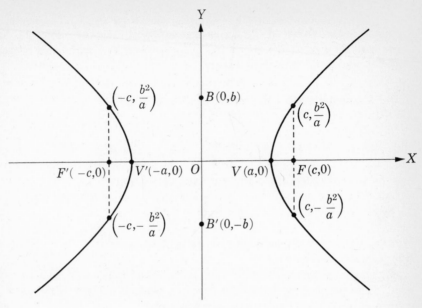

FIGURE 5–15

a, b, and c as used in connection with the hyperbola is not the same as for the ellipse. For the ellipse we chose $a > b$ and defined c by the equation $c^2 = a^2 - b^2$; for the hyperbola c is defined by $c^2 = a^2 + b^2$ and no restriction is placed on the relative values of a and b.

The hyperbola

$$\frac{y^2}{a^2} - \frac{x^2}{b^2} = 1 \tag{11}$$

has its vertices at $V'(0,-a)$ and $V(0,a)$, and the foci are at $F'(0,-c)$ and $F(0,c)$, where still $c^2 = a^2 + b^2$.

EXAMPLE. Find the equation of the hyperbola with foci at $(0,\pm 5)$ and a vertex at $(0,3)$.

Solution. The location of the foci shows that the equation is of the form (11). Using $c = 5$ and $a = 3$ in the relation $c^2 = a^2 + b^2$, we find $b^2 = 16$. Hence the desired equation is

$$\frac{y^2}{25} - \frac{x^2}{16} = 1.$$

5–9 The asymptotes of a hyperbola. Unlike the other conic sections, the hyperbola has associated with it two lines which are its asymptotes. In this connection the quantity b, which seems to have no immediate geometrical interpretation, becomes significant. To draw the asymptotes, we first construct the rectangle (Fig. 5-16) with a pair of sides through the vertices perpendicular to the transverse axis and the other sides through $(0,-b)$ and $(0,b)$. The extended diagonals of this rectangle are the asymptotes of the hyperbola of equation (10). To show that these lines are asymptotes, we first consider the diagonal and the part of the hyperbola extending into the first quadrant. The equations of the diagonal and this part of the hyperbola are, respectively,

$$y = \frac{b}{a} x \qquad \text{and} \qquad y = \frac{b}{a} \sqrt{x^2 - a^2}.$$

We see that for any $x > a$ the ordinate of the hyperbola is less than the ordinate of the line. If, however, x is many times as large as a, the corresponding ordinates are almost equal. This may be seen more convincingly by examining the difference of the two ordinates. Thus by subtracting and changing the form, we get

$$\frac{b(x - \sqrt{x^2 - a^2})}{a} = \frac{b(x - \sqrt{x^2 - a^2})(x + \sqrt{x^2 - a^2})}{a(x + \sqrt{x^2 - a^2})} = \frac{ab}{x + \sqrt{x^2 - a^2}}.$$

The numerator of the last fraction is constant. The denominator increases as x increases, and can be made as large as we please by taking x sufficiently large. Therefore the difference of the ordinates approaches zero. Since the perpendicular distance from a point of the hyperbola to the line is less than the difference in y-values, the line is an asymptote of the curve. From considerations of symmetry we conclude that the extended diagonals are asymptotes to the hyperbola in each of the four quadrants. The equation of the other diagonal is of course $y = -(b/a)x$.

Similarly, the equations of the asymptotes of the hyperbola (11) are

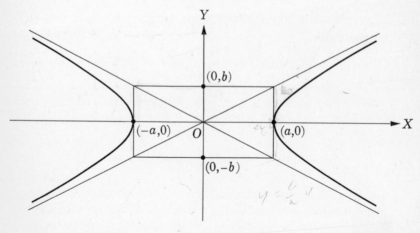

FIGURE 5-16

$$y = \frac{a}{b}\,x \qquad \text{and} \qquad y = -\frac{a}{b}\,x.$$

We observe that for each of the hyperbolas (10) and (11) the asymptotes may be obtained by factoring the left member and equating each factor to zero.

The asymptotes are helpful in sketching a hyperbola. A rough drawing can be made from the associated rectangle and its extended diagonals. The accuracy may be improved considerably, however, by plotting the end points of each latus rectum.

If $a = b$, the associated rectangle is a square and the asymptotes are perpendicular to each other. For this case the hyperbola is called *equilateral* because its axes are equal, or is named *rectangular* because its asymptotes intersect at right angles.

The ratio c/a is called the *eccentricity* e of the hyperbola. The angle of intersection of the asymptotes, and therefore the shape of the hyperbola, depends on the value of e. Since c is greater than a, the value of e is greater than 1. If c is just slightly greater than a, so that e is near 1, the relation $c^2 = a^2 + b^2$ shows that b is small compared with a. Then the asymptotes make a pair of small angles. The branches of the hyperbola, enclosed by small angles, diverge slowly. If e increases, the branches are enclosed by larger angles. And the angles can be made near 90° by taking large values for e.

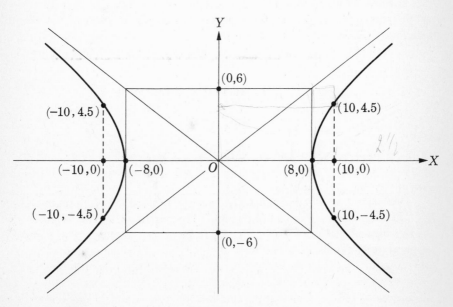

FIGURE 5-17

EXAMPLE.   Sketch the curve $36x^2 - 64y^2 = 2304$.

Solution.   Dividing by 2304 reduces the given equation to the form

$$\frac{x^2}{64} - \frac{y^2}{36} = 1.$$

Here $a = 8$, $b = 6$, and from $c^2 = a^2 + b^2$, we find $c = 10$.   The vertices therefore are $(\pm 8, 0)$ and the foci are $(\pm 10, 0)$.   Each latus rectum has a length of 9 units. The equations of the asymptotes are $3x - 4y = 0$ and $3x + 4y = 0$.   From this information the hyperbola can be drawn (Fig. 5–17).

EXERCISE 5–3

For each hyperbola 1–8 find the coordinates of the vertices and foci, the length of each latus rectum, and the equations of the asymptotes.   Sketch each curve, using the asymptotes.

1. $\dfrac{x^2}{16} - \dfrac{y^2}{9} = 1$.

2. $\dfrac{x^2}{36} - \dfrac{y^2}{64} = 1$.

3. $\dfrac{y^2}{9} - \dfrac{x^2}{4} = 1$.

4. $\dfrac{y^2}{9} - \dfrac{x^2}{25} = 1$.

5. $\dfrac{x^2}{4} - \dfrac{y^2}{21} = 1$.

6. $\dfrac{x^2}{20} - \dfrac{y^2}{16} = 1$.

7. $y^2 - x^2 = 36$.

8. $x^2 - y^2 = 49$.

Write the equations of the hyperbolas whose axes are on the coordinate axes, and which also satisfy the conditions given in problems 9–16.

9. Vertex $(4,0)$; end of conjugate axis $(0,3)$.

10. Focus $(6,0)$; vertex $(4,0)$.

11. Focus $(0,5)$; conjugate axis 4.

12. Conjugate axis 6; vertex $(7,0)$.

13. Latus rectum 5; focus $(3,0)$.

14. End of conjugate axis $(3,0)$; length of latus rectum 10.

15. Passes through $(6,5)$ and $(8, 2\sqrt{15})$.

16. Passes through $(3, \sqrt{2})$ and $(2\sqrt{3}, 2)$.

5–10 Applications of conics.   Many examples of conics have been discovered in natural phenomena, and important applications of them abound in engineering and industry.

A projectile, as a ball or bullet, travels in a path which is approximately a parabola.   The paths of some comets are nearly parabolic.   Cables of some suspension bridges hang in the form of a parabola.   The surface generated by revolving a parabola about its axis is called a paraboloid of revolution.   A reflecting surface in this form has the property that light emanating at the focus is reflected in the direction of the axis.   This kind of surface is used in headlights, in some telescopes, and in devices to reflect sound waves.   A comparatively recent application of parabolic metal surfaces is found in radar equipment. The surfaces reflect radio waves in the same way that light is reflected, and are used in directing outgoing beams and also in receiving waves from other stations.

The planets have elliptic paths with the sun at a focus. Much use is made of semi-elliptic springs and elliptic-shaped gears. A surface of the form made by revolving an ellipse about its major axis is so shaped that sound waves emanating at one focus are reflected to arrive at the other focus. This principle is illustrated in whispering galleries and other buildings.

A very interesting and important application of the hyperbola is that of locating the place from which a sound, as of a gun, emanates. From the difference in the times at which the sound reaches two listening posts, the difference between the distances of the posts from the gun can be determined. Then, knowing the distance between the posts, the gun is located on a branch of a hyperbola of which the posts are foci. The position of the gun on this curve can be found by the use of a third listening post. Either of the two posts and the third are foci of a branch of another hyperbola on which the gun is located. Hence the gun is at the intersection of the two branches.

The principle used in finding the location of a gun is also employed by a radar-equipped airplane to determine its location. In this case the plane receives radio signals from three stations of known locations.

5-11 Standard forms of second degree equations. In our study of conics thus far we have dealt with simple forms of the second degree equation. Any conic, as we learned in Section 4-4, can be represented by one of these special equations if the coordinate axes are located properly with respect to the curve. We now know the location of the axes with respect to the conics which are represented by the simple equations (5)-(11). For the central conics (ellipse and hyperbola) the axes of the conic are on the coordinate axes and the center and origin therefore coincide. In the case of the parabola the axis is on one of the coordinate axes and the vertex and origin coincide. In view of this information concerning conics and the coordinate axes, we can interpret geometrically the transformations by which second degree equations are reduced to the simple forms. The rotation which removes the product term in the equation of a conic orients the coordinate axes in the directions of the axes of a central conic (ellipse and hyperbola) or, in the case of a parabola, makes one axis parallel to the axis of the parabola. Having eliminated the product term, the translation to remove the first degree terms, or one first degree term and the constant term, brings the origin of coordinates to the center of the central conic and, in the case of the parabola, to the vertex.

The simplified forms of the equations of conics which we have used in this chapter are of great advantage in drawing the graphs and studying their properties. However, it is necessary in many situations to deal with equations in more complicated forms. The known quantities in a given problem may lead to a second degree equation which at first is not obtainable in simplified form. For example, the original information concerning a body moving along a parabola may not give the location of the vertex or the direction of the axis. To start the investigation the coordinate axes would need to be chosen to fit the known quantities. Also, a single problem may involve two conics whose axes are not in the same directions and whose centers do not coincide.

Since it is sometimes necessary to deal with equations of conics which are not in the simplest forms, we next consider equations whose forms are more general. We begin with equations which have no xy term. In this case a translation of axes would reduce an equation to one of the simple forms. Hence we consider equations which would be reduced to the simple forms by a translation of the origin to a point (h,k). We obtain these equations from the simple forms by replacing x by $x - h$ and y by $y - k$.

$$(y - k)^2 = 4a(x - h), \tag{12}$$

$$(x - h)^2 = 4a(y - k), \tag{13}$$

$$\frac{(x - h)^2}{a^2} + \frac{(y - k)^2}{b^2} = 1, \tag{14}$$

$$\frac{(y - k)^2}{a^2} + \frac{(x - h)^2}{b^2} = 1, \tag{15}$$

$$(x - h)^2 + (y - k)^2 = a^2, \tag{16}$$

$$\frac{(x - h)^2}{a^2} - \frac{(y - k)^2}{b^2} = 1, \tag{17}$$

$$\frac{(y - k)^2}{a^2} - \frac{(x - h)^2}{b^2} = 1. \tag{18}$$

These equations are said to be in *standard forms*. By translating the origin to the point (h,k), each reduces to one of the simple forms. The quantities a and b are unchanged in meaning. Constructing the graph of an equation in one of these standard forms presents no greater difficulty than drawing the graph of the corresponding simple form.

Equation (14), for example, represents an ellipse with its center at the point (h,k). The major axis has a length of $2a$ and is parallel to the x-axis. The distance from the center to a focus is c, where $c = a^2 - b^2$. If $a = b$, equation (14) reduces to the form (16), which represents a circle of radius a with its center at (h,k).

Equation (13) represents a parabola with a vertical axis and has only one y-value for each value of x. This fact is also evident when the equation is solved for y. Thus we obtain an equation of the form

$$y = Ax^2 + Dx + F.$$

Here y is expressed as a quadratic function of x. We may now conclude that a quadratic function of x has either a greatest or a least value, since the graph is a parabola with a vertical axis. Hence an equation of the form (13) displays the coordinates of the maximum or the minimum point of the graph of a quadratic function of x. In Chapter 6 we shall develop a general method for finding the maximum and minimum points of the graphs of quadratic and certain other functions of a variable.

EXAMPLE 1. Sketch the graph of the equation

$$y^2 + 8x - 6y + 25 = 0.$$

Solution. We recognize the equation as representing a parabola. The graph may be more readily drawn if we first reduce the equation to standard form. Thus

$$y^2 - 6y + 9 = -8x - 25 + 9,$$
$$(y - 3)^2 = -8(x + 2).$$

The vertex is at $(-2,3)$. Since $4a = -8$ and $a = -2$, the focus is 2 units to the left of the vertex. The length of the latus rectum, numerically equal to $4a$, is 8. This means that the latus rectum extends 4 units above the focus and 4 units below. The graph is constructed in Fig. 5–18.

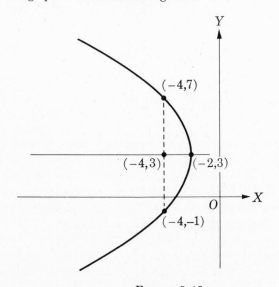

FIGURE 5–18

EXAMPLE 2.   Find the equation of the ellipse with foci at $(4,-2)$ and $(10,-2)$, and a vertex at $(12,-2)$.

Solution.   The center, midway between the foci, is at $(7,-2)$.   The distance between the foci is 6 and the given vertex is 5 units from the center; this makes $c = 3$ and $a = 5$.   Then $b^2 = a^2 - c^2 = 16$.   Hence the desired equation is

$$\frac{(x-7)^2}{25} + \frac{(y+2)^2}{16} = 1.$$

5–12 The addition of ordinates.   The presence of an xy-term in the equation of a conic usually makes the construction of the graph much more difficult.   Preparing a table of corresponding values of the variables is tedious since, in general, a quadratic equation with irrational roots needs to be solved for each pair of values.   Another plan would be to rotate the axes and use the new equation and the new axes to draw the graph.   But rotation transformations are not short and usually the process is complicated by cumbersome radicals in the rotation formulas.   For some equations the *addition of ordinates* method can be used advantageously.   The principle involved in this process is that the graph of the sum of two functions can be obtained by adding the ordinates of the separate graphs of the functions.   The utility of the method depends on the ease with which the separate graphs are obtained.

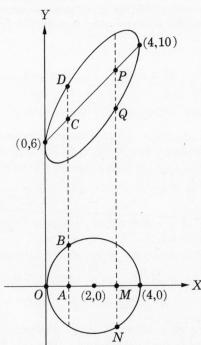

FIGURE 5–19

EXAMPLE.   Draw the graph of the equation

$$2x^2 - 2xy + y^2 + 8x - 12y + 36 = 0.$$

Solution.   To express y as the sum of two functions of x, we treat the equation as a quadratic in y. Thus we have

$$y^2 + (-2x - 12)y + (2x^2 + 8x + 36) = 0,$$

and solving for y gives

$$y = \frac{2x + 12 \pm \sqrt{(-2x - 12)^2 - 4(2x^2 + 8x + 36)}}{2} = x + 6 \pm \sqrt{4x - x^2}.$$

We now draw the graphs of the equations

$$y = x + 6 \qquad \text{and} \qquad y = \pm\sqrt{4x - x^2}.$$

The locus of the first equation is a line. By squaring and then completing the square in the x-terms, the second equation becomes $(x - 2)^2 + y^2 = 4$. The graph is a circle of radius 2 and center at (2,0). The line and circle are drawn in Fig. 5–19. The point D on the graph of the given equation is obtained by adding the ordinates AB and AC. That is, AC is extended by a length equal to AB. The addition of ordinates for this purpose must be algebraic. Thus MN is negative and the point Q is found by measuring downward from P so that $PQ = MN$. By plotting a sufficient number of points in this manner the desired graph can be drawn.

The graph, obtained from a second degree equation, is by definition a conic. From the shape we conclude that the given equation represents an ellipse. In the following section we show that this conclusion can be drawn immediately from the equation itself.

5–13 Identification of a conic.   The kind of conic represented by an equation of the form

$$Ax^2 + Bxy + Cy^2 + Dx + Ey + F = 0$$

can be determined immediately from the coefficients of the second degree terms. We already know how to identify the type of conic if $B = 0$. If $B \neq 0$, we rotate the axes through an angle θ (Section 4–4) and obtain

$$A'x'^2 + B'x'y' + C'y'^2 + D'x' + E'y' + F' = 0,$$

where

$$A' = A \cos^2 \theta + B \sin \theta \cos \theta + C \sin^2 \theta,$$
$$B' = \cos 2\theta - (A - C) \sin 2\theta,$$
$$C' = A \sin^2 \theta - B \sin \theta \cos \theta + C \cos^2 \theta.$$

If $B'^2 - 4A'C'$ is computed, the result, when simplified, is

$$B'^2 - 4A'C' = B^2 - 4AC.$$

This relation among the coefficients of the original equation and the transformed equation holds for any rotation. For this reason the expression

$B^2 - 4AC$ is called an *invariant*. By selecting the particular rotation for which $B' = 0$, we have

$$-4A'C' = B^2 - 4AC.$$

With $B' = 0$ the kind of conic represented by the transformed equation, and therefore the original equation, can be determined from the signs of A' and C'. The conic is an ellipse if A' and C' have like signs, and a hyperbola if the signs are different. If either A' or C' is zero, the conic is a parabola. These relations of A' and C', in the order named, would make $-4A'C'$ negative, positive, or zero. Hence we have the following important theorem.

THEOREM. *The graph of $Ax^2 + Bxy + Cy^2 + Dx + Ey + F = 0$, when it exists, is an ellipse, hyperbola, or a parabola according as $B^2 - 4AC$ is negative, positive, or zero.*

It must be remembered that in this theorem the degenerate conics are included. These exceptional cases are indicated in the following résumé:

$B^2 - 4AC < 0$, ellipse or an isolated point,

$B^2 - 4AC > 0$, hyperbola or two intersecting lines,

$B^2 - 4AC = 0$, parabola, two parallel lines, or one line.

EXERCISE 5-4

In each problem 1–4 write the equation of the circle which satisfies the given conditions.

1. Center $(2,-6)$; radius 5.   2. Center $(0,0)$; radius 3.

3. Center $(0,4)$; radius 4.   4. Center $(-2,0)$; radius 7.

5. The segment joining $A(0,0)$ and $B(8,-6)$ is a diameter.

6. The segment joining $A(-5,1)$ and $B(7,5)$ is a diameter.

Reduce the equations 7–10 to standard forms. Sketch the graph in each case by the use of the vertex and the ends of the latus rectum.

7. $y^2 - 12x - 8y + 4 = 0$.   8. $x^2 + 12x - 4y + 36 = 0$.

9. $4x^2 + 12x - 16y + 41 = 0$.   10. $y^2 - 7x + 21 = 0$.

Find the equations of the parabolas determined by the conditions given in problems 11–14. Sketch each parabola.

11. Vertex $(2,3)$; focus $(5,3)$.   12. Vertex $(-2,1)$; focus $(-2,-1)$.

13. Vertex $(0,2)$; axis vertical; length of latus rectum 16.

14. Vertex $(-2,1)$; axis horizontal; passes through $(0,-4)$.

Reduce equations 15–18 to standard forms. In each find the coordinates of the center, the vertices, the foci, and the ends of the minor axis. Sketch each curve.

15. $16x^2 + 25y^2 - 160x - 200y + 400 = 0$.

16. $9x^2 + 25y^2 - 36x - 189 = 0$.

17. $3x^2 + 2y^2 - 24x + 12y + 60 = 0$.

18. $4x^2 + 8y^2 + 4x + 24y - 13 = 0$.

Write the equation of the ellipse which satisfies the conditions in each problem 19–22. Sketch each ellipse.

19. Center (5,1); vertex (5,4); end of minor axis (3,1).

20. Vertex (6,3); foci (−4,3) and (4,3).

21. Ends of minor axis (−1,2) and (−1,−4); focus (−1,1).

22. Vertices (−1,3) and (5,3); length of minor axis 4.

Reduce equations 23–26 to standard forms. In each find the coordinates of the center, the vertices, and the foci. Describe the locus of each equation.

23. $9x^2 - 16y^2 - 54x - 63 = 0$.

24. $21x^2 - 4y^2 + 84x - 32y - 64 = 0$.

25. $5y^2 - 4x^2 - 30y - 32x = 99$.

26. $2y^2 - 3x^2 - 8y + 6x - 1 = 0$.

Write the equations of the hyperbolas which satisfy the conditions given in problems 27–30.

27. Center (1,3); vertex (4,3); end of conjugate axis (1,1).

28. Vertex (−4,0); foci (−5,0) and (1,0).

29. Ends of conjugate axis (3,−1) and (3,5); focus (−1,2).

30. Vertices (−1,3) and (5,3); length of conjugate axis 6.

Sketch the graph of each equation 31–36 by the addition of ordinates method.

31. $y = x \pm \sqrt{x}$.

32. $y = 6 - x \pm \sqrt{4 - x^2}$.

33. $y = 2x \pm \sqrt{5 + 6x - x^2}$.

34. $y^2 - 2xy + 2x^2 - 1 = 0$.

35. $x^2 - 2xy + y^2 - 4x - 12 = 0$.

36. $2x^2 + 2xy + y^2 + 8x + 4y + 4 = 0$.

Assuming that each equation 37–42 represents a nondegenerate conic, classify each by computing $B^2 - 4AC$.

37. $2x^2 - 4xy + 8y^2 + 7 = 0$.

38. $3x^2 + xy + x - 4 = 0$.

39. $2xy - x + y - 3 = 0$.

40. $x^2 + 5xy + 15y^2 = 1$.

41. $x^2 - y^2 + 4 = 0$.

42. $x^2 - 2xy + y^2 + 3x = 0$.

43. $3x^2 + 6xy + 3y^2 - x + y = 0$.

44. $4x^2 - 3xy + y^2 + 13 = 0$.

45. Determine whether the equation $x^2 - xy - 2y^2 + x - 2y = 0$ represents a hyperbola or two intersecting lines by treating the equation as a quadratic in x and solving for x in terms of y.

46. Solve the equation $x^2 + 2xy + y^2 - 2x - 2y + 1 = 0$ for one variable in terms of the other. Is the locus a parabola or a degenerate conic?

47. Work out all the steps in showing that $B'^2 - 4A'C' = B^2 - 4AC$.   Show also that $A' + C' = A + C$.

Find the greatest or least value of each function 48 and 49.   Draw the graph and estimate the zeros of the function.

48. $x^2 - 7x + 4$.   49. $5 - 2x - 2x^2$.

50. Listening posts are at A, B, and C.   Point A is 2000 feet north of point B, and point C is 2000 feet east of B.   The sound of a gun reaches A and B simultaneously one second after it reaches C.   Show that the coordinates of the gun's position are approximately $(860,1000)$, where the x-axis passes through B and C and the origin is midway between B and C.   Assume that sound travels 1100 feet per second.

CHAPTER 6

THE SLOPE OF A CURVE

6–1 An example. The graph of $y = x^2$ is shown in Fig. 6–1. Suppose that we draw a line through the point $P(1,1)$ of the graph and a neighboring point Q of the graph with abscissa $1 + h$. The ordinate of Q, obtained by replacing x by $1 + h$ in the equation, is $(1 + h)^2$. Hence the slope of the line is given by

$$m = \frac{y_2 - y_1}{x_2 - x_1} = \frac{(1 + h)^2 - 1}{(1 + h) - 1} = \frac{2h + h^2}{h} = (2 + h)\frac{h}{h}.$$

The slope is thus expressed in terms of h. The quantity h may be assigned any value except zero. This value is avoided because division by zero is not permissible, and also because P and Q would then be the same point and would not determine a line. Agreeing that $h \neq 0$, we substitute 1 for h/h in the expression for the slope, and have $m = 2 + h$. While h must not be zero, it may be as near zero as we please. A value of h near zero makes the slope of the line through P and Q near 2. In fact, the slope can be brought arbitrarily near 2 by taking h small enough. We see also that when h is small Q is near P, and it can be made to take a position as close to P as we please. Consider now the line through P with the slope 2 and denote the line by L. A line through P and Q can be obtained which is arbitrarily near coincidence with L. This situation is described by saying that as h approaches zero (or as Q approaches P) the line L is the limit-

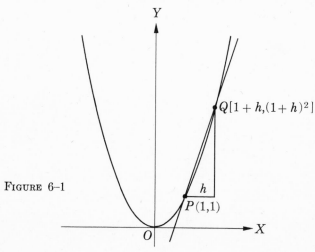

FIGURE 6–1

ing position of the line determined by P and Q. A line such as L is of special significance and is given a name in the following paragraph.

Let P and Q be two points of a curve. The line through P and Q is called a *secant line*. Keeping P fixed, let Q move along the curve and approach P. The secant line will, in the curves which we shall study, revolve about P and approach a limiting position as Q is brought arbitrarily close to P. The limiting position of the secant line is called the *tangent* to the curve at the point P.

In accordance with this definition, the line through P (Fig. 6–1) with slope 2 is tangent to the curve. The curve is also said to have slope 2 at P. More generally, the *slope of a curve* at any point is defined to be equal to the slope of the tangent at the point.

Still using the equation $y = x^2$, we next let $P(x,y)$ stand for any point of the curve. If we take $x + h$ as the abscissa of another point Q of the curve, the corresponding ordinate is $(x + h)^2$. The slope of the line through P and Q (Fig. 6–2) is

$$m = \frac{(x + h)^2 - x^2}{(x + h) - x} = \frac{2hx + h^2}{h} = (2x + h)\frac{h}{h}.$$

Hence, if $h \neq 0$, $m = 2x + h$. This slope can be made as near $2x$ as we please by taking h small enough. Therefore we say that the line through P with slope $2x$ is the tangent to the curve at P. Thus we see that the slope of the tangent, and also the slope of the curve, at any point is twice the abscissa of the point. This means that the curve has negative slopes to the left of the origin, zero slope at the origin, and positive slopes to the right of the origin. We see also that the curve gets steeper as x increases numerically. The steepness of the curve is a measure of the rate of change of the ordinate relative to a change in the value of the abscissa.

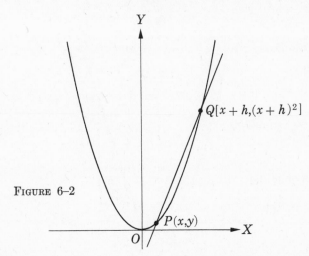

FIGURE 6–2

By means of the slope expression we gain considerable information about the graph.

In this chapter we shall make use of the slope in studying the characteristics of the graph of a function. This is a fundamental and powerful concept of mathematics.

6–2 Limits. In the preceding example we observed that $(2x + h)h/h$ can be made arbitrarily close to $2x$ by taking h small. The expression $2x$ is said to be the *limit* of the original expression as h approaches zero. We state this fact symbolically as

$$\lim_{h \to 0} (2x + h)\frac{h}{h} = 2x.$$

Although h approaches zero, we specify that it is not to be given the value zero. This means that $(2x + h)h/h$ is not equal to $2x$, but can be made as close as we please to $2x$ by choosing h small enough.

As a further illustration, we find the limit of

$$\frac{(x + h)^3 - x^3}{h}$$

as h approaches zero. Here the result is not immediately evident. The limit can easily be found, however, if we first cube the binomial. Thus we have

$$\lim_{h \to 0} \frac{(x + h)^3 - x^3}{h} = \lim_{h \to 0} \frac{x^3 + 3x^2h + 3xh^2 + h^3 - x^3}{h}$$
$$= \lim_{h \to 0} (3x^2 + 3xh + h^2)\frac{h}{h}$$
$$= \lim_{h \to 0} (3x^2 + 3xh + h^2)$$
$$= 3x^2.$$

6–3 The derivative. Consider now the more general equation

$$y = f(x),$$

where the right member is some function of x. Let P and Q be two points of the graph of the equation which have abscissas x and $x + h$. The corresponding ordinates are $f(x)$ and $f(x + h)$. Hence the slope of the line through P and Q (Fig. 6–3) is

$$\frac{f(x + h) - f(x)}{(x + h) - x} = \frac{f(x + h) - f(x)}{h}.$$

The line through P with slope equal to

$$\lim_{h \to 0} \frac{f(x + h) - f(x)}{h}$$

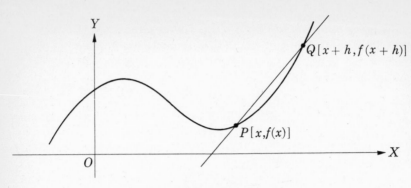

FIGURE 6–3

is called the *tangent* to the curve at P. The slope of the curve at P is defined to be the slope of the tangent.

The name *derivative* is given to the limit just mentioned, and $D_x f(x)$ is one notation for the limit or derivative. That is,

$$D_x f(x) = \lim_{h \to 0} \frac{f(x + h) - f(x)}{h}.$$

Other notations for the derivative of $f(x)$ in $y = f(x)$ are

$$f'(x), \quad \frac{df(x)}{dx}, \quad D_x y, \quad y', \quad \text{and} \quad \frac{dy}{dx}.$$

The derivative is a fundamental concept in calculus and has numerous important applications. We shall make use of the derivative in the study of a very restricted class of functions. A preliminary task in this connection is the derivation of formulas by which the derivative of a function may be written at sight.

6–4 Derivative formulas. We first work out the derivative of ax^n, where a is a constant and n is a positive integer. From the definition of derivative,

$$D_x ax^n = \lim_{h \to 0} \frac{a(x + h)^n - ax^n}{h}.$$

To evaluate the limit, we expand $(x + h)^n$ by the binomial theorem, collect like terms, and divide the numerator and denominator by h. Thus

$$\frac{a(x + h)^n - ax^n}{h} = \frac{a}{h} \left[x^n + nx^{n-1}h + \frac{n(n - 1)}{2} x^{n-2}h^2 + \cdots + h^n - x^n \right]$$

$$= a \left[nx^{n-1} + \frac{n(n - 1)}{2} x^{n-2}h + \cdots + h^{n-1} \right].$$

The last expression has h as a factor in all terms except the first. Hence the limit, as h approaches zero, of each term after the first is zero. The limit of the sum of these terms is also zero. Hence we have

$$D_x ax^n = nax^{n-1}. \tag{1}$$

Notice that this formula permits us to write at once the derivative of a constant times a positive integral power of x. We multiply by the exponent and decrease the power of x by one unit. In terms of slope, this means that the graph of $y = ax^n$ has at any point (x,y) the slope nax^{n-1}. If $n = 1$, formula (1) becomes

$$D_x ax = ax^0 = a.$$

The derivative for this case is constant, as would be expected, since $y = ax$ is a straight line with the slope a.

Illustrations. $D_x 5x^3 = 15x^2$; $D_x(-2x^4) = -8x^3$; $D_x x^5 = 5x^4$; $D_x 3x = 3$.

We next find the derivative of a constant. That is, we let

$$f(x) = C,$$

where C is a constant. This means that $f(x)$ has the same value for all values of x, and therefore $f(x + h) = C$. Hence

$$\frac{f(x + h) - f(x)}{h} = \frac{C - C}{h} = \frac{0}{h}.$$

Since h approaches zero but is not to assume the value zero, the quantity $0/h$ is zero for all permissible values of h. We therefore conclude that

$$D_x C = 0. \tag{2}$$

This result is in agreement with what we would expect, because the derivative is the slope of the graph of the function. The graph of $f(x) = C$ is a line parallel to the x-axis and the slope is zero at all its points.

An expression of the form

$$a_0 x^n + a_1 x^{n-1} + a_2 x^{n-2} + \cdots + a_{n-1}x + a_n,$$

where the a's are constants with $a_0 \neq 0$, is a polynomial in x of the nth degree. We now know how to write the derivative of each term of a polynomial. The question then arises if the sum of the derivatives of the separate terms is equal to the derivative of the sum of the terms. This may be proved to be true. We shall make the assumption, omitting the proof.

We have established formula (1) for any positive integer n. In calculus the formula is proved to hold for any real number n. We shall use the formula for positive and negative integral exponents. The proof for a negative integral exponent could be made by starting with the definition of derivative and proceeding somewhat as in the case of a positive integral exponent. We omit the proof, however.

EXAMPLE 1. Find the derivative of the polynomial

$$4x^5 - 3x^4 + x^3 - 7x + 5.$$

Solution. To find the derivative, we apply formula (1) to each term containing x and formula (2) to the constant term 5. Hence

$$D_x(4x^5 - 3x^4 + x^3 - 7x + 5) = 20x^4 - 12x^3 + 3x^2 - 7.$$

EXAMPLE 2. Write the derivative of $3x^{-4} - \dfrac{5}{x^3} + \dfrac{1}{x} - x - 3.$

Solution. We change the fractional terms to $-5x^{-3}$ and x^{-1} and apply formulas (1) and (2). This gives

$$D_x(3x^{-4} - 5x^{-3} + x^{-1} - x - 3) = -12x^{-5} + 15x^{-4} - x^{-2} - 1.$$

EXAMPLE 3. Find the slope of the curve

$$y = x^3 - 3x^2 + 4$$

at the point $P(3,4)$. Write the equation of the tangent at this point.

Solution. We obtain the derivative (or slope expression) by using formulas (1) and (2). Thus

$$D_x y = 3x^2 - 6x.$$

The slope at the point P is obtained by substituting 3 for x in the derivative. Hence the desired slope is $27 - 18 = 9$. The equation of the line through $(3,4)$ with slope 9 is

$$9x - y - 23 = 0.$$

EXERCISE 6-1

Find the limits indicated in problems 1–6.

1. $\lim\limits_{x \to 2} (x^2 - 4).$

2. $\lim\limits_{x \to 0} \dfrac{x + 2}{x + 1}.$

3. $\lim\limits_{x \to -2} (2x - 1).$

4. $\lim\limits_{h \to 0} \dfrac{2(x + h) - 2x}{h}.$

5. $\lim\limits_{h \to 0} \dfrac{(x + h)^4 - x^4}{h}.$

6. $\lim\limits_{h \to 0} \left(\dfrac{1}{x + h} - \dfrac{1}{x} \right) \dfrac{1}{h}.$

Find $f'(x)$ in each problem 7–20.

7. $f(x) = 2x - 4.$

8. $f(x) = 5 - 6x.$

9. $f(x) = x^3.$

10. $f(x) = 5x^3.$

11. $f(x) = 3x^2 - 4x.$

12. $f(x) = x^3 - 4x^2 + 3x.$

13. $f(x) = x^{-3}.$

14. $f(x) = 5x^{-1} + x.$

15. $f(x) = \dfrac{1}{x}.$

16. $f(x) = 4x^5 + x^4 - 2x^3 + 6x^2.$

17. $f(x) = 3x^{-4} - 5x^{-2} + 2.$

18. $f(x) = -\dfrac{3}{x^3}.$

19. $f(x) = \dfrac{1}{x^4}.$

20. $f(x) = 1 + \dfrac{2}{x} + \dfrac{3}{x^2} + \dfrac{4}{x^3}.$

In each equation 21–30 find $D_x y$ and the equation of the tangent at the given point.

21. $y = x^2;\ (1,1).$

22. $y = x^2 + 3;\ (0,3).$

23. $y = \dfrac{1}{x};\ (-1,-1).$

24. $y = \dfrac{3}{x^2};\ (1,3).$

25. $y = x^2 - 4x;\ (2,-4).$

26. $y = x^3 - 6x^2 + 8x;\ (0,0).$

27. $y = x^4 - 4x^2;\ (2,0).$

28. $y = 2x^{-2} + 3x;\ (x = 2).$

29. $y = x^{-4} + x^4;\ (x = -1).$

30. $y = 1 + \dfrac{2}{x} + \dfrac{3}{x^2};\ (x = -2).$

6–5 The use of the derivative in graphing. We now consider the derivative as an aid in studying the behavior of functions and in constructing their graphs. Before examining particular functions, however, we look for the meaning of the sign of the derivative at a point of the curve. The graph of $y = f(x)$ is shown in Fig. 6–4, and tangents are drawn at the indicated points A, B, C, and D. If we think of a point as moving along the curve from left to right, we notice that the moving point would be rising at some positions and falling at others. At points on the curve where the moving point is rising, we say that y is an *increasing function* of x. That is, y increases as x increases. At points where the moving point is falling, y is a *decreasing function*. At A the function $f(x)$ is an increasing function. Here the slope of the curve, $D_x y$, is a positive number. The function is decreasing at C, and the derivative is negative. The slope, and also the derivative, is zero at B and D. The points B and D separate rising and falling portions of the curve. We conclude that a positive derivative at a point indicates that the point is on a portion of the curve which rises toward the right. That is, the function increases as x in-

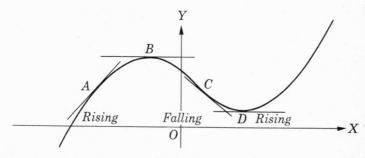

FIGURE 6–4

creases. A negative derivative indicates a decreasing function; the curve falls toward the right.

EXAMPLE 1. Find the values of x for which the graph of $5 + 4x - x^2$ has positive slopes, zero slope, or negative slopes.

Solution. We let y stand for the function and write

$$y = 5 + 4x - x^2.$$

For the derivative, we have

$$D_x y = 4 - 2x = 2(2 - x).$$

We note that the derivative is equal to zero when $x = 2$, is positive for $x < 2$, and is negative for $x > 2$. That is,

$$D_x y > 0, \quad \text{when} \quad x < 2,$$
$$D_x y = 0, \quad \text{when} \quad x = 2,$$
$$D_x y < 0, \quad \text{when} \quad x > 2.$$

Since the derivative expression gives the slope of the graph of the function, we see that the graph has positive slopes to the left of $x = 2$, zero slope at $x = 2$, and negative slopes to the right of $x = 2$. This tells us that the curve is rising at points to the left of $x = 2$ and falling at points to the right of $x = 2$. Hence the graph has its greatest height at $x = 2$. Substituting 2 for x in the given function, we find the functional value, y, to be 9. Hence the point $(2,9)$ is the peak point of the graph, and 9 is the greatest value of the given function.

Noticing the derivative $2(2 - x)$ further, we observe that at a point far to the left of $x = 2$ the derivative is a large number, indicating that the curve is steep. Similarly, the curve gets steeper and steeper as x increases beyond 2. The steepness of the curve gives a measure of the rate of change in y relative to an increase in x.

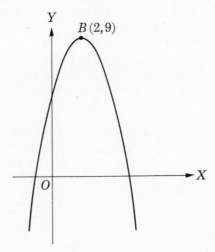

FIGURE 6–5

This examination of the derivative furnishes information which is helpful in drawing the graph (Fig. 6–5).

EXAMPLE 2.   Examine the function $x^3 - 6x^2 + 9x - 1$ and construct its graph.

Solution.   Letting y stand for the function, we have

$$y = x^3 - 6x^2 + 9x - 1$$

and then

$$D_x y = 3x^2 - 12x + 9 = 3(x - 1)(x - 3).$$

We see at once that the derivative is zero when $x = 1$ and when $x = 3$.   To find the intervals of positive and negative slopes, we first notice the signs of the factors $x - 1$ and $x - 3$ of the derivative.   The factor $x - 1$ is negative if $x < 1$ and positive for values of $x > 1$.   The factor $x - 3$ is negative for $x < 3$ and positive if $x > 3$.   Both factors are negative to the left of $x = 1$, and hence their product is positive.   For x between 1 and 3, $x - 1$ is positive and $x - 3$ is negative, giving a negative product.   Both factors are positive to the right of $x = 3$.   We write this information in the following symbolic form.

$$\begin{aligned}
D_x y &= 0, & \text{when} && x &= 1, \\
D_x y &= 3(+)(-) < 0, & \text{when} && 1 &< x < 3, \\
D_x y &= 0, & \text{when} && x &= 3, \\
D_x y &= 3(+)(+) > 0, & \text{when} && x &> 3.
\end{aligned}$$

We now interpret this information relative to the graph.   Since the derivative is positive for $x < 1$, the curve to the left of $x = 1$ is rising toward the right.   The negative derivative at points between 1 and 3 signify a falling curve.   The derivative is zero at $x = 1$, and this point separates rising and falling portions of the curve.   Hence the graph is higher at $x = 1$ than at points to the left or at points just to the right.   The corresponding ordinate is 3, and therefore the point $A(1,3)$ is a peak point.   Similarly, the derivative is negative at points between $x = 1$

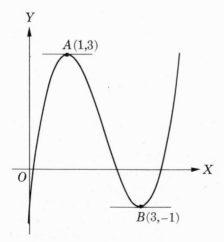

FIGURE 6–6

and $x = 3$, is zero at $x = 3$, and is positive at points to the right of $x = 3$. When $x = 3$, $y = -1$, hence the point $B(3, -1)$ of the graph is lower than those immediately to the left and lower than those to the right. The curve gets steeper and steeper as points are taken farther and farther to the left of A, and the steepness also increases as x increases beyond 3.

With the preceding information and just a few plotted points a good graph can be constructed (Fig. 6–6).

6–6 Maximum and minimum points. In the two preceding problems we found points of the curves where the slope is zero. Each of these points marks the transition from positive to negative or negative to positive slopes. In other words, each is a high or low point compared with those nearby. The location of these points helped tremendously in drawing the graphs. Later we shall see that the points which separate rising and falling portions of the curve are of special significance in applied problems. We wish now to give names to points of this kind and to outline a procedure for finding them.

A function $y = f(x)$ is said to have a relative *maximum* at $x = a$ if the value of $f(x)$ is greater when $x = a$ than when x has values slightly less or slightly more than a. More specifically, $f(x)$ has a maximum at $x = a$ if

$$f(a) > f(a + h)$$

for all negative and positive values of h sufficiently near zero. This situation is pictured in Fig. 6–7 by the point A. The value of the function at the point A is greater than its values at neighboring points both to the left and right. The value at A, however, is not the greatest of all values of the function, since a part of the curve extends higher than A. The word *relative* is used to indicate that the ordinate of a maximum point is considered relative to the ordinates of neighboring points. The greatest of all values which a function has in its range is sometimes called an *absolute* maximum. For example, the function pictured in Fig. 6–5 has an absolute maximum at the point B.

The function $f(x)$ has a relative *minimum* at $x = a$ if

$$f(a) < f(a + h)$$

for all values of h close enough to zero. If the inequality holds for *all* positive and negative values of h, the minimum is an absolute minimum. A minimum point is shown at B. Here the slope of the curve is zero. The point B is a transition point from negative to positive slopes.

At C the slope is zero, but this is neither a maximum nor a minimum point. We notice that the slope immediately to the left is positive and is also positive to the right. Hence the tangent at C cuts through the curve and the slope does not change in sign as x increases through this point.

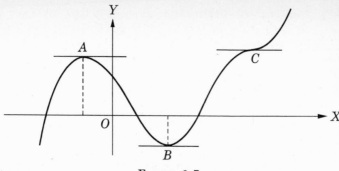

FIGURE 6–7

From Fig. 6–7 we may, intuitively at any rate, outline a procedure for finding the maximum and minimum points of the graph of a function.

1. *Set the derivative equal to zero to find the abscissas of points where the slope is zero.*

2. *Suppose the slope is zero at $x = a$.   Determine the sign of the derivative for values of x slightly less than a and the sign for values slightly more than a.*

3. *If the sign changes from positive to negative in passing from the left to the right, the function has a maximum at $x = a$.   If the sign changes from negative to positive, the function has a minimum at $x = a$.   The maximum or minimum is the value of the function when $x = a$.   If the sign does not change, the function has neither a maximum nor a minimum at $x = a$.*

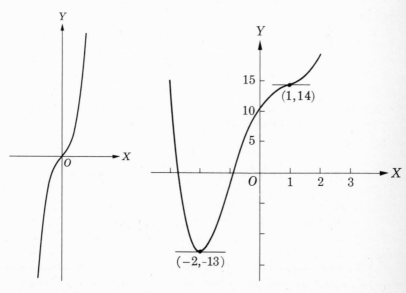

FIGURE 6–8　　　　　　　　　　FIGURE 6–9

EXAMPLE 1. Show that the slope of $y = x^3 + x$ is everywhere positive.

Solution. We find
$$D_x y = 3x^2 + 1.$$

The derivative is positive for all real values of x. Figure 6–8 shows the graph.

EXAMPLE 2. Find and test for maximum and minimum values the points of zero slope of
$$y = x^4 - 6x^2 + 8x + 11.$$

Solution. Taking the derivative, we find
$$D_x y = 4x^3 - 12x + 8 = 4(x^3 - 3x + 2) = 4(x + 2)(x - 1)^2.$$

The slope is zero at $x = -2$ and $x = 1$. We notice that the derivative is negative for values of x less than -2 and positive for values of x slightly greater than -2. Hence the function has a minimum value when $x = -2$. The minimum value, found by substituting -2 for x, is -13. The factor $(x - 1)^2$ is positive for all values of x except 1. The slope of the curve, therefore, does not change sign in passing through $x = 1$. The tangent line (Fig. 6–9) cuts through the graph at $(1,14)$.

EXERCISE 6–2

Find the coordinates of points of zero slope in problems 1–14. Tell in each case if the point is a maximum or minimum point. Give the intervals of positive and negative slopes. Draw the curves.

1. $y = 2 - x^2$.
2. $y = x^2$.
3. $y = x^2 - 4x$.
4. $y = 2x^2 - 2x$.
5. $y = 1 + 6x - x^2$.
6. $y = 1 + 2x - \frac{1}{4}x^2$.
7. $y = -x^3$.
8. $y = x^3 + 3x$.
9. $y = \frac{1}{3}x^3 - x^2 + x$.
10. $y = x^3 - 6x^2 + 9x - 3$.
11. $y = 2x^3 + 3x^2$.
12. $y = 3x^2 - x^3$.
13. $y = x^3 - 3x^2 + 4$.
14. $y = 2 + 3x - x^3$.

Find the coordinates of the points of zero slope, and make a rough sketch of the graph in problems 15–22.

15. $y = 3x^4 - 4x^3$.
16. $y = x^4 + 2x^2$.
17. $y = \frac{x^4}{4} - \frac{2x^3}{3} + \frac{x^2}{2} + 1$.
18. $y = \frac{x^4}{4} - \frac{x^3}{3} - \frac{x^2}{2} + x$.
19. $y = \frac{x^4}{4} - x^3 + x^2 + 1$.
20. $y = x^4 - 2x^2 + 1$.
21. $y = \frac{x^4}{4} + \frac{x^3}{3} - \frac{x^2}{2} - x$.
22. $y = \frac{x^4}{4} - \frac{x^3}{3} - 2x^2 + 4x$.

6–7 Applications. There are many practical problems whose solutions involve maximum and minimum values of functions. The following examples illustrate the procedure for handling some problems of this kind.

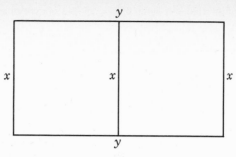

FIGURE 6–10

EXAMPLE 1. A farmer has 600 rods of fencing. He wishes to enclose a rectangular pasture and divide the area into two equal parts by a fence parallel to two opposite sides. Find the dimensions of the pasture if the area is to be a maximum.

Solution. We let x and y stand for the dimensions (Fig. 6–10). We note that by choosing the y-dimension near 300 the x-dimension would be near zero, giving a very narrow rectangle of little area. By letting x increase from near zero to a length near 200, the shape of the rectangle would vary and again become quite narrow, with the y-dimension near zero. Hence we suspect that the area is greatest for x somewhere between 0 and 200.

If A indicates the area, we have

$$A = xy.$$

It is desirable to obtain A in terms of one variable, either x or y. Hence we next find a relation between x and y. From the figure, $3x + 2y$ is the total length of the fence. Therefore

$$3x + 2y = 600, \quad \text{and} \quad y = 300 - \tfrac{3}{2}x.$$

Substituting for y, we have

$$A = x\left(300 - \frac{3x}{2}\right) = 300x - \frac{3}{2}x^2.$$

To find the value of x which makes A a maximum, we set $D_xA = 0$ and solve for x. Thus

$$D_xA = 300 - 3x,$$

$$300 - 3x = 0, \quad \text{and} \quad x = 100.$$

When $x = 100$, $y = 150$, and $A = 15,000$ square rods. From the nature of the problem, we surmise that the area is a maximum for these dimensions. This may be verified by noting that the derivative is positive for x less than 100 and negative for x greater than 100.

The function $300x - \tfrac{3}{2}x^2$ is a complete parabola if x is not restricted in value.

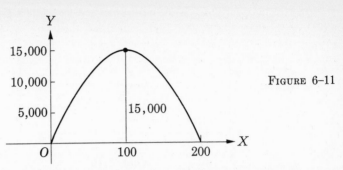

FIGURE 6–11

In our problem, however, x may take only the values between 0 and 200. The graph for this range of x is drawn in Fig. 6–11.

EXAMPLE 2. A cylindrical can without a top is to have a capacity of 1000π cubic inches. Find the radius and height if the amount of material is to be a minimum.

Solution. If we let x stand for the radius, y for the height, and S for the cylindrical area plus the area of the circular bottom, we have

$$S = \pi x^2 + 2\pi xy.$$

To express S in terms of one variable, we substitute the value of y in terms of x. We have

$$\pi x^2 y = 1000\pi, \quad \text{and} \quad y = \frac{1000}{x^2},$$

and hence

$$S = \pi x^2 + \frac{2000\pi}{x} = \pi x^2 + 2000\pi x^{-1},$$

$$D_x S = 2\pi x - 2000\pi x^{-2} = 2\pi \frac{x^3 - 1000}{x^2}.$$

We see that $D_x S = 0$, when $x = 10$. The corresponding value of y is 10. The least amount of material is required when the radius is 10 inches and the height also 10 inches.

EXERCISE 6–3

1. What is the largest rectangular area which can be enclosed with 400 yards of fence?

2. Divide the number 8 into two parts such that the sum of their squares is a minimum.

3. A rectangular pasture is to be fenced along four sides and divided into three equal parts by two fences parallel to one of the sides. Find the greatest area if 800 yards of fence are to be used.

4. A rectangular plot is to contain 5 acres (800 sq. rds.) and to be fenced off along a straight river bank. What dimensions will require the least amount of fencing? No fence is used along the river.

5. A rectangular box is to be made from a sheet of tin 8 inches by 12 inches by cutting square pieces from each corner and then turning up the sides. For what depth will the volume of the box be a maximum?

6. A box with a square base and open top is to be made from 27 square feet of material. Find the dimensions if the volume is to be a maximum.

7. An uncovered rectangular water tank is to be lined with sheet copper. If the tank is to hold 108 cubic feet of water and the base is a square, find the dimensions for a minimum amount of sheet copper.

8. A closed cylindrical can is to be made from 24π square inches of sheet tin. Find the radius and height in order for the volume to be a maximum.

9. A closed cylindrical can is to be made to contain 16π cubic inches. What should be the radius and height for the amount of tin to be a minimum?

10. A window is formed by a rectangle surmounted by a semicircle and has a perimeter of 12 feet. Find the dimensions to admit the most light.

11. The combined length and girth of a parcel post package must not exceed 100 inches. What is the volume of the largest box with a square base that can be sent by parcel post?

CHAPTER 7

TRANSCENDENTAL FUNCTIONS

7–1 Introduction. An equation in which all terms are of the form ax^my^n, where a is a constant and each exponent is a positive integer or zero, is an algebraic equation in x and y. Either variable may be regarded as an algebraic function of the other. The functions which we have studied are algebraic. In this chapter we shall take up functions which are not algebraic. Functions which are not algebraic are classed as *transcendental*. The most common transcendental functions, and those which we shall study, are the trigonometric, the inverse trigonometric, the exponential, and the logarithmic functions. These functions are of tremendous importance; they are used extensively in physics, engineering, probability, and statistics.

7–2 The trigonometric curves. Before constructing the graphs of the trigonometric functions we shall point out a certain property which these functions possess. A function $f(x)$ is said to be *periodic* if there is a constant p such that for all values of x

$$f(x) = f(x + p).$$

The smallest positive value of p for which this is true is called the *period*. The trigonometric functions are periodic. The sine function, for example, satisfies the equations

$$\sin x = \sin (x + 2\pi) = \sin (x + 2n\pi),$$

where x is any angle in radians and n is an integer. Thus the values of the sine of an angle recur in intervals of 2π radians. This recurrence does not take place in smaller intervals, and hence 2π is the period of the sine function. This is also the period of the cosine, secant, and cosecant of an angle. The period of the tangent and cotangent of an angle is π. For these functions we have the identities

$$\tan x = \tan (x + \pi) \qquad \text{and} \qquad \cot x = \cot (x + \pi).$$

In drawing the graph of a trigonometric function, advantage should be taken of its periodic nature. If the graph is obtained for an interval equal to its period, then this part of the graph can be reproduced in other intervals to the right and left. To plot points for drawing the curve over an interval of one period, the values of the function corresponding to values of the angle can be had from a table of trigonometric functions (see Appendix).

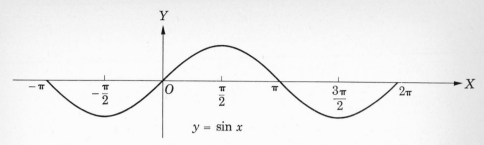

$y = \sin x$

FIGURE 7–1

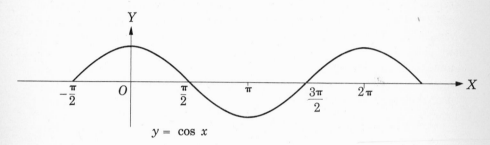

$y = \cos x$

FIGURE 7–2

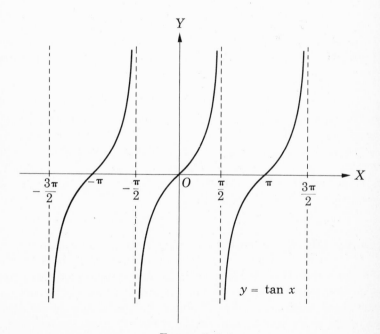

$y = \tan x$

FIGURE 7–3

Figures 7–1 and 7–2 show the graphs of $y = \sin x$ and $y = \cos x$. Each of these curves crosses the x-axis after every π radians of x-values. The ordinates of each vary from -1 to 1. These are called the *extreme* values, and the constant 1 is called the *amplitude*.

The tangent curve (Fig. 7–3) crosses the x-axis at integral multiples of π radians and has asymptotes at odd integral multiples of $\frac{1}{2}\pi$ radians. Amplitude is not defined for the tangent.

The secant curve (Fig. 7–4) has no x-intercepts. The asymptotes occur after every π radians of x-values.

We next consider the function $a \sin bx$, where a and b are constants. Since the extreme values of $\sin bx$ are -1 and 1, the extreme values of $a \sin bx$ are $-a$ and a. The amplitude is equal to the absolute value of a. To find the period, we determine how much x changes in producing a

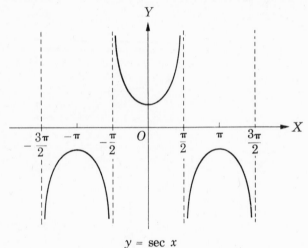

$y = \sec x$

FIGURE 7–4

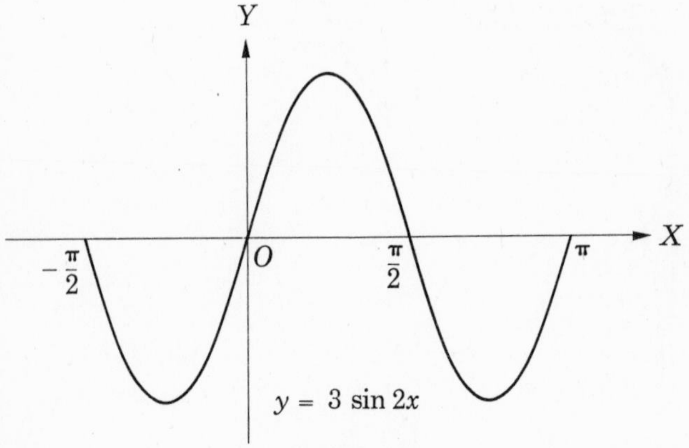

$y = 3 \sin 2x$

FIGURE 7–5

change of 2π in the angle bx.   As x varies from 0 to $2\pi/b$, the angle bx increases from 0 to 2π.   Hence the period of sin bx is $2\pi/b$.   As an illustration, 3 sin $2x$ has an amplitude of 3 and a period of π.   The graph of $y = 3$ sin $2x$ is drawn in Fig. 7–5.

7–3 The inverse trigonometric functions.   The graphs of the inverse trigonometric functions may be obtained readily from the graphs of the direct functions.   To draw the graph of $y =$ arc sin x, for example, we recall that the equations

$$y = \text{arc sin } x \qquad \text{and} \qquad x = \sin y$$

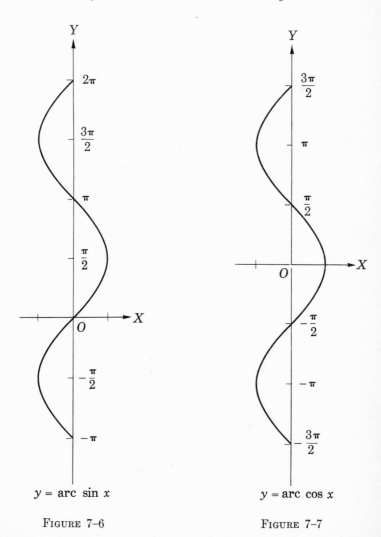

$$y = \text{arc sin } x$$

FIGURE 7–6

$$y = \text{arc cos } x$$

FIGURE 7–7

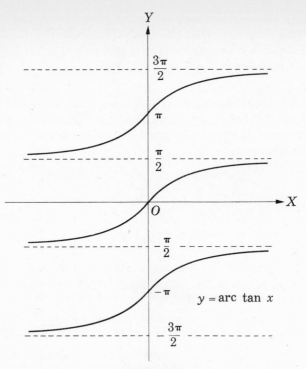

FIGURE 7–8

express the same relation between x and y.   Hence the graphs of these two equations must coincide.   The equations

$$x = \sin y \qquad \text{and} \qquad y = \sin x$$

have x and y interchanged.   The graph of $y = \sin x$ (Fig. 7–1) winds along the x-axis.   We conclude, therefore, that the graph of $x = \sin y$ is a curve of the same form winding along the y-axis.   The graph of $x = \sin y$, or $y = \arc \sin x$, is shown in Fig. 7–6.

The graphs of each of the other inverse functions can be found similarly from the graph of the direct function by reversing the roles of x and y. Figures 7–7 and 7–8 show the graphs of $y = \arc \cos x$ and $y = \arc \tan x$.

EXERCISE 7–1

Find the period of each function 1–12.   Give the amplitudes of the sine and cosine functions.

1. $\cos 3x$.

2. $\sin \frac{1}{2}x$.

3. $\sin \frac{1}{3}x$.

4. $2 \cos 4x$.

5. $\tan 5x$.

6. $\cot \frac{1}{4}x$.

7. $\sec 6x$.

8. $\cos 7x$.

9. $\tan \frac{3}{4}x$.

10. $3 \cos \pi x$.

11. $2 \sin \frac{1}{2}\pi x$.

12. $\sec (\frac{1}{2}x + \frac{1}{2}\pi)$.

Sketch the graph of each equation 13–24.

13. $y = 3 \cos x$.   14. $y = 2 \sin x$.   15. $y = \sin 3x$.

16. $y = \cos 2x$.   17. $y = \tan 2x$.   18. $y = \cot x$.

19. $y = 3 \sin \frac{1}{2}x$.   20. $y = 4 \tan \frac{2}{3}x$.   21. $y + 4 \sin \frac{3}{2}x$.

22. $y = \tan \frac{1}{2}x$.   23. $y = \csc x$.   24. $y = 5 \sin 4x$.

Draw the graphs of the inverse trigonometric equations 25–30.

25. $y = 2 \text{ arc } \cos x$.   26. $y = 3 \text{ arc } \sin x$.

27. $y = 2 \text{ arc } \tan x$.   28. $y = \frac{1}{2} \text{ arc } \cos \frac{1}{2}x$.

29. $y = 3 \text{ arc } \sin \frac{1}{2}x$.   30. $y = \frac{1}{2} \text{ arc } \tan 2x$.

7–4 The exponential curves. An equation in which a variable or a function of a variable is an exponent is called an *exponential equation*. The corresponding graph is known as an *exponential curve*. The equations

$$y = 2^x, \qquad y = e^x, \qquad \text{and} \qquad y = 10^x$$

are simple exponential equations. Each could be made more general by replacing the exponent by a less simple function of x.

The letter e in the second equation stands for an irrational number approximately equal to 2.71828. This number is of great importance in

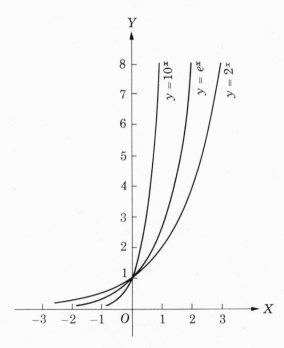

FIGURE 7–9

advanced mathematics, and exponential functions involving e as a base have wide applications in both theory and practice.

The graph of $y = e^x$ can be drawn by using the table (see Appendix) to find values of y for assigned values of x. Corresponding values of y in the equations $y = 2^x$ and $y = 10^x$ are simply obtained when x is an integer. To determine other pairs of values a table of logarithms can be used. Figure 7–9 has the graph of the three equations drawn in the same coordinate system for purposes of comparison.

7–5 Logarithmic curves. If a is a positive number different from 1 and y is any real number in the equation $a^y = x$, then y is called the logarithm of x to the base a. This relation may be written symbolically as $y = \log_a x$. Thus the two equations

$$a^y = x \qquad \text{and} \qquad y = \log_a x$$

express the same relation among the numbers a, x, and y. The first is in exponential form and the second in logarithmic form. Since the base a is positive, a^y also has a positive value. Hence we shall consider the logarithms of positive numbers only.

Since a logarithmic equation can be changed to an exponential equation, it appears that logarithmic and exponential curves must be closely related. To see the relation, we note that the logarithmic equation $y = \log_a x$ is equivalent to, and therefore has the same graph as, $x = a^y$. Now the equations

$$x = a^y \qquad \text{and} \qquad y = a^x$$

are alike except that x and y play reverse roles. Hence their graphs must have the same form but different positions relative to the coordinate axes.

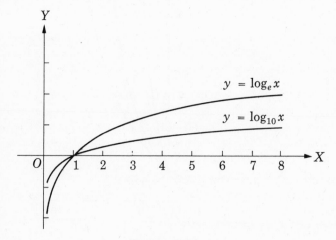

FIGURE 7–10

The most frequently used bases for logarithms are the numbers 10 and e. A table of logarithms can be used for drawing the curve corresponding to a logarithmic equation employing either of these bases. Corresponding values of x and y for the equations $y = \log_{10} x$ and $y = \log_e x$ are here tabulated with the logarithmic values rounded off to one decimal place. These should be verified by referring to the tables in the Appendix. The graphs are drawn in Fig. 7–10.

x	.01	.1	.2	.5	.8	1	2	4	8	10
$\log_{10} x$	-2.0	-1.0	$-.7$	$-.3$	$-.1$	0	.3	.6	.9	1.0
$\log_e x$	-4.6	-2.3	-1.6	$-.7$	$-.2$	0	.7	1.4	2.1	2.3

EXERCISE 7–2

Sketch the graphs of the following equations:

1. $y = 4^x$.
2. $y = 4^{-x}$.
3. $y = 2e^x$.
4. $y = e^{2x}$.
5. $y = e^{x^2}$.
6. $y = e^{-x^2}$.
7. $y = 2^{2x-1}$.
8. $y = 2^{x^2-x}$.
9. $y = xe^x$.
10. $y = 3 \log_{10} x$.
11. $y = 2 \log_e x$.
12. $y = \log_{10} (-x)$.
13. $y = \log_e (-x)$.
14. $y = \log_{10} 4x$.
15. $y = \log_e x^2$.
16. $y = \log_2 x$.
17. $y = \log_{10} (x - 3)$.

18. Show that the graph of $y = \log_a bx$ is the graph of $y = \log_a x$ shifted vertically a distance of $\log_a b$.

19. Show that the graph of $y = \log_a x^2$ can be obtained by doubling each ordinate of $y = \log_a x$.

20. If \$100 is invested at 2% per year compounded continuously, the accumulated amount y at the end of x years is given by the equation

$$y = 100e^{0.02x}.$$

Sketch the graph of this equation and from the graph estimate the accumulated amount at the end of (a) 3 years, (b) 6 years, (c) 9 years. Estimate also the time required for the original investment to double.

7–6 The graph of the sum of two functions. The addition of ordinates method can sometimes be efficiently applied to draw the graph of the sum of two functions in which one or both are transcendental. The process is exactly that used in Section 5–12 and is illustrated by the following example involving a transcendental function.

EXAMPLE 1. Sketch the graph of the equation

$$y = \sqrt{x} + \sin x.$$

Solution. We first draw the graphs of

$$y = \sqrt{x}, \quad \text{and} \quad y = \sin x.$$

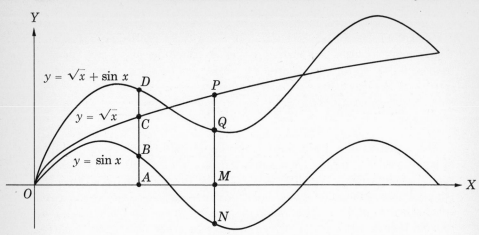

FIGURE 7–11

The locus of the first of these equations is the upper half of the parabola $y^2 = x$, and the second yields the sine curve; both are familiar and easily sketched. The two curves are shown in Fig. 7–11. The point D on the graph of the given equation is obtained by adding the ordinates AB and AC. That is, AC is extended by a length equal to AB. The addition of ordinates for this purpose must be algebraic. Thus MN is negative and the point Q is found by measuring downward from P so that $PQ = MN$. By plotting a sufficient number of points in this way the desired graph can be drawn.

EXERCISE 7–2

Sketch the graph of each of the following equations by the addition of ordinates method.

1. $y = x + \sin x.$ 2. $y = x - \cos x.$

3. $y = \sqrt{x} + \cos x.$ 4. $y = \sin x + \cos x.$

5. $y = \sin x + \cos 2x.$ 6. $y = 2 \sin x + \sin 2x.$

7. $y = x + \log_{10} x.$ 8. $y = x + e^x.$

9. $y = \frac{1}{2}(e^x + e^{-x}).$ 10. $y = e^x + \log_{10} x.$

CHAPTER 8

EQUATIONS OF CURVES AND CURVE FITTING

8–1 Equation of a given curve. Having obtained curves as the graphs of equations, it is natural to surmise that a curve in a plane has a corresponding equation. We shall first consider the problem of writing the equation of a curve all of whose points are definitely fixed by certain given geometric conditions. The graph of the resulting equation should be in exact agreement with the given curve. In other words, the equation of a curve is a relation between x and y which is satisfied by the coordinates of all points, and only those points, which belong to the given curve.

In the latter part of this chapter we shall consider the problem of finding the equation when the original information locates certain points (usually a few) but does not establish any particular curve.

EXAMPLE 1. A point moves so that its distance from the fixed point $F(2,0)$ divided by its distance from the y-axis is always equal to $\frac{1}{2}$. Find the equation of the locus of the moving point.

Solution. We select a typical point P of the path (Fig. 8–1). Then $2FP = DP$ expresses the required relation between the distances. In terms of the coordinates x and y of the variable point P, this relation is

$$2\sqrt{(x-2)^2 + y^2} = x,$$

or, by simplification,

$$3x^2 + 4y^2 - 16x + 16 = 0.$$

This is the equation of an ellipse, since x^2 and y^2 have unequal coefficients of the same sign.

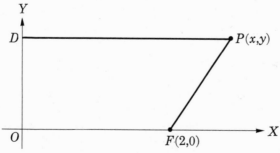

FIGURE 8–1

EXAMPLE 2. Find the equation of the circle which passes through the points $(-2,-2)$, $(5,-3)$, and $(2,1)$.

Solution. The equation of the circle can be written in the form

$$x^2 + y^2 + Dx + Ey + F = 0.$$

Our problem is to find values for D, E, and F so that this equation is satisfied by the coordinates of the given points. Hence we substitute for x and y the coordinates of these points. This gives the system

$$4 + 4 - 2D - 2E + F = 0,$$
$$25 + 9 + 5D - 3E + F = 0,$$
$$4 + 1 + 2D + E + F = 0.$$

The solution of these equations is $D = -3$, $E = 5$, and $F = -4$. Therefore the required equation is

$$x^2 + y^2 - 3x + 5y - 4 = 0.$$

EXERCISE 8–1

In each problem 1–14 find the equation of the locus of $P(x,y)$ which satisfies the given condition.

1. P is 5 units from the fixed point $(2,-3)$.

2. P is equidistant from $(2,-4)$ and $(-1,5)$.

3. The abscissa of P is equal to its distance from the point $(3,2)$.

4. P is on the circle with center at $(3,-2)$ and which passes through $(6,2)$.

5. P is the vertex of a right triangle whose hypotenuse is the segment joining $(-5,0)$ and $(5,0)$.

6. The sum of the squares of the distances between P and the points $(4,2)$ and $(-3,1)$ is 50.

7. P is twice as far from $(0,3)$ as from $(3,0)$.

8. P is three times as far from $(1,1)$ as from $(-3,4)$.

9. P is equidistant from $(-8,1)$ and the y-axis.

10. P is twice as far from the x-axis as from $(0,3)$.

11. P is twice as far from $(5,0)$ as from the y-axis.

12. The sum of the distances from P to $(0,-3)$ and to $(0,3)$ is 10.

13. The difference of the distances from P to $(-5,0)$ and to $(5,0)$ is numerically equal to 8.

14. The angle $APB = 45°$, where A and B are the points $(-1,0)$ and $(1,0)$.

15. A point moves so that its distance from a fixed point divided by its distance from a fixed line is always equal to a constant e. Find the equation of the path of the moving point. *Suggestion:* Take the y-axis along the fixed line and the x-axis through the fixed point, say $(k,0)$. From the resulting equation observe that the path is a parabola if $e = 1$, an ellipse if e is between zero and 1, and a hyperbola if e is greater than 1. Show that for $e \neq 1$ the x-intercepts (vertices) are $k/(1 + e)$ and $k/(1 - e)$. Where is the center of the conic? Divide the dis-

tance between the center and $(k,0)$ by the distance between the center and one of the x-intercept points. Do you conclude that $(k,0)$ is a focus and e is the eccentricity?

16. Find the equation of the circle which passes through the points $(3,0)$, $(4,2)$, and $(0,1)$.

17. Find the equation of the circle which passes through $(0,0)$, $(5,0)$, and $(3,3)$.

18. Find the equation of the parabola $y = ax^2 + bx + c$ which passes through $(0,6)$, $(-1,2)$, and $(-2,6)$.

19. Find the equation of the parabola $y = ax^2 + bx + c$ which passes through $(0,0)$, $(1,-1)$, and $(-1,5)$.

8–2 Equation corresponding to empirical data.

We now take up a much different and more difficult aspect of the problem of finding equations representing known information. Here the problem is not primarily of geometric interest but one in which analytic geometry is fruitful in aiding the scientist. Experimental scientists make observations and measurements of various kinds of natural phenomena. Measurements in an investigation often represent two variable quantities which are functionally related. In many situations the study can be advanced through an equation which expresses the relation, or an approximate relation, between the two variables in question. The equation can then be used to compute corresponding values of the variables other than those obtained by measurement. The equation is called an *empirical equation*, and the process employed is called *curve fitting*.

Suppose, for example, that various loads are placed at the mid-point of a beam supported at its ends. If for each load the deflection of the beam at its mid-point is measured, then a series of corresponding values are obtained. One value of each pair is the load and the other the deflection produced by the load. The table gives readings where x stands for the load in pounds and y the deflection in inches. Taking the loads as abscissas and the deflections as ordinates, the pairs of values are plotted as points

x	100	120	140	160	180	200
y	0.45	0.55	0.60	0.70	0.80	0.85

in Fig. 8–2. The points lie almost in a straight line, and suggest that the deflection is a linear function of the load. That is, an equation of the form

$$y = mx + b$$

gives the relation, or an approximate relation, between the load and the deflection. Since the points are not exactly in a straight line, no linear equation can be satisfied by all pairs of the readings. We are then faced with the problem of selecting a particular linear equation. A line could be drawn by sight so that it passes quite close to each point. It is de-

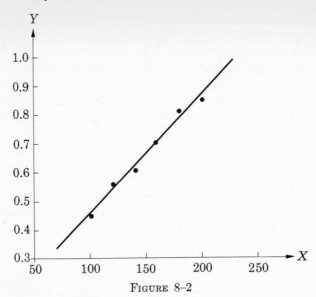

FIGURE 8–2

sirable, however, to follow some procedure which will locate a definite line. In the next section we shall discuss a method of determining a line which is called the *best fitting line* for a set of data.

If the points representing a set of data are not approximately in a straight line, a linear equation will not express well the relation between the variables. It would then be necessary to use some nonlinear relation in looking for a satisfactory equation. The most common nonlinear functions are the polynomial, trigonometric, inverse trigonometric, exponential, and logarithmic functions. A set of data might be represented by one of these functions or a combination of them. Thus the first step in a curve fitting problem is the selection of some type of function. The second step is the determination of some particular function of the type selected which will furnish a satisfactory representation of the data. We shall deal with the second part of the problem by employing a process called the *method of least squares*. The first step, namely, the choice of a type, will be considered later.

8–3 The method of least squares. Suppose that we have given n points in a plane whose coordinates are (x_1, y_1), (x_2, y_2), $\cdots$, (x_n, y_n). We define the *residual* of each of the points relative to a curve as the ordinate of the point minus the ordinate of the curve for the same x-value. The totality of residuals may be examined to determine if the curve is a good fit to the points. A curve is considered a good fit if each of the residuals is small. Since some of the residuals could be positive and others negative, their sum might be near zero for a curve which is a poor fit to the points. Hence the sum of the residuals would not furnish a reliable measure of the accuracy of fit. For this reason we shall deal with the squares of the residuals, thus avoiding negative quantities. If the sum of the squares of the residuals is small, we would know that the curve passes close to each of the n points. The better fitting of two curves of the same type is the one for which the sum of the squares of the residuals is smaller. The best fitting curve of a given type is the one for which the sum of the squares of the residuals is a minimum.

Starting with the simplest situation, we shall show how to determine the best fitting line to the n given points. We write the linear equation

$$y = mx + b,$$

where values are to be found for m and b so that the sum of the squares of the residuals of the n points is a minimum. The residual of the point (x_1, y_1) is $y_1 - (mx_1 + b)$. The quantity y_1 is the ordinate of the point, and $(mx_1 + b)$ is the ordinate of the line when $x = x_1$. Hence the residuals of the points are

$$y_1 - (mx_1 + b), \; y_2 - (mx_2 + b), \cdots, y_n - (mx_n + b),$$

and their squares are

$$y_1{}^2 - 2mx_1y_1 - 2y_1b + m^2x_1{}^2 + 2mx_1b + b^2,$$
$$y_2{}^2 - 2mx_2y_2 - 2y_2b + m^2x_2{}^2 + 2mx_2b + b^2,$$
$$\cdots \cdots \cdots \cdots \cdots \cdots \cdots \cdots \cdots$$
$$y_n{}^2 - 2mx_ny_n - 2y_nb + m^2x_n{}^2 + 2mx_nb + b^2.$$

To express the sum of these expressions in a convenient form, we use the following notation.

$$\Sigma x = x_1 + x_2 + \cdots + x_n,$$
$$\Sigma x^2 = x_1{}^2 + x_2{}^2 + \cdots + x_n{}^2,$$
$$\Sigma xy = x_1y_1 + x_2y_2 + \cdots + x_ny_n.$$

Denoting the sum of the squares of the residuals by R, we have

$$R = \Sigma y^2 - 2m\Sigma xy - 2b\Sigma y + m^2\Sigma x^2 + 2mb\Sigma x + nb^2.$$

We notice that all quantities in R are fixed except m and b. For example, Σy^2 is not a variable; it stands for the sum of the squares of the ordinates of the n fixed points.

Our problem now is to determine values for m and b which make R a minimum. The expression for R contains the first and second powers of both m and b. If b is assigned any value whatever, then R is a quadratic function of m. Hence the graph of the function is a parabola. Choosing the m-axis as horizontal and treating b as an unspecified constant, the parabola has a vertical axis and extends upward. The parabola opens upward because R, being the sum of squared expressions, is not negative.

Consequently the least value of R is the ordinate of the vertex. If we set m equal to its value at the vertex, a relation is obtained which must be satisfied in order that R shall be a minimum. This equation, as we shall see, involves both m and b. In a similar way, considering R a quadratic function of b, a second relation between m and b may be obtained. The simultaneous solution of these equations yields formulas for m and b.

In Section 5–11 we learned how to find the coordinates of the vertex of a parabola. We also learned, in Chapter 6, that differentiation may be applied to find maximum and minimum points of a graph. The differentiation process is employed below. As an exercise, the reader might work through the alternative method.

First, treating b as constant, we find D_mR. Next, we differentiate to obtain D_bR, where m is considered constant. These derivatives, by the procedure of Section 6–6, are to be equated to zero. Thus we have

$$D_mR = -2\Sigma xy + 2m\Sigma x^2 + 2b\Sigma x = 0,$$
$$D_bR = -2\Sigma y + 2m\Sigma x + 2nb = 0.$$

Solving these equations simultaneously for m and b, we have

$$m = \frac{n\Sigma xy - \Sigma x\Sigma y}{n\Sigma x^2 - (\Sigma x)^2}, \quad b = \frac{\Sigma x^2\Sigma y - \Sigma x\Sigma xy}{n\Sigma x^2 - (\Sigma x)^2}. \tag{1}$$

These formulas enable us to compute m and b for the line of best fit to a set of given points. We illustrate their use in an example.

EXAMPLE. Find the line of best fit to the data plotted in Fig. 8–2.

Solution. For these data $n = 6$, and computing the required sums appearing in formulas (1), we obtain

$\Sigma x = 100 + 120 + 140 + 160 + 180 + 200 = 900,$
$\Sigma y = 0.45 + 0.55 + 0.60 + 0.70 + 0.80 + 0.85 = 3.95,$
$\Sigma x^2 = 100^2 + 120^2 + 140^2 + 160^2 + 180^2 + 200^2 = 142,000,$
$\Sigma xy = 100(.45) + 120(.55) + 140(.60) + 160(.70) + 180(.80) + 200(.85) = 621.$

These results, substituted in formulas (1) for m and b, yield

$$m = \frac{6(621) - 900(3.95)}{6(142,000) - 900^2} = \frac{171}{42,000} = 0.0041,$$
$$b = \frac{142,000(3.95) - 900(621)}{42,000} = 0.048.$$

Using these values for m and b, the equation of the line of best fit to the data is

$$y = 0.0041x + 0.048.$$

This equation gives approximately the relation between the load and deflection and holds for loads which do not bend the beam beyond its elastic limits. The deflection produced by a load of 400 pounds, for example, is $y = 0.0041(400) + 0.048 = 1.69$ inches. The data and the line are shown graphically in Fig. 8–2.

Find the equation of the line of best fit to the sets of points in problem 1 and in problem 2.   Plot the points and draw the line.

1. (1,8), (4,6), (5,5), (8,3), (9,2), (11,1).

2. (−2,−10), (0,−5), (1,0), (2,5), (4,8).

3. The lengths y (inches) of a coiled spring under various loads x (lb) are recorded in the table.   Find the line of best fit, $y = mx + b$, for these measurements.   Use the resulting equation to find the length of the spring when the load is 17 pounds.

x	10	20	30	40	50
y	11.0	12.1	13.0	13.9	15.1

4. A business showed net profits at the end of each year for 4 years as follows:

Year	1	2	3	4
Profit	$10,000	$12,000	$13,000	$15,000

Determine the best linear fit and predict the profit for the 5th year.

5. The population N of a city at the end of each decade t for 5 decades is shown in the table.   Find the line of best fit, $N = mt + b$, for these data.   Predict the population at the end of the 6th decade.

t	1	2	3	4	5
N	8,000	9,000	10,100	11,400	13,700

6. The relation between the total amount of heat H in a pound of saturated steam at T degrees centigrade is $H = mT + b$.   Determine m and b for the best linear fit to these data.

T	50	70	90	110
H	623	627	632	636

8–4 Nonlinear fits.   A best linear fit may be obtained for any set of points (x,y).   However, if the points depart considerably from a straight line, the fit would be crude and perhaps far from satisfactory.   For a situation of this kind the scientist needs to decide on some nonlinear relation.   There are, of course, many nonlinear functional forms.   We shall deal only with the forms

$$y = ax^b,$$
$$y = a \cdot 10^{bx},$$
$$y = a \log x + b.$$

Numerous physical relations approximately obey one of these types of equations. These equations are advantageous because of their simplicity and because the constants a and b are easily determined.

8–5 The power formula. We consider first the relation

$$y = ax^b.$$

The logarithms of the members of the equation yield

$$\log y = b \log x + \log a.$$

Here $\log y$ is expressed as a linear function of $\log x$. This suggests the plotting of the points ($\log x$, $\log y$). If the points so obtained lie approximately on a line, the power function is applicable to the set of data. The procedure then is to determine a and b for the best linear fit to the points ($\log x$, $\log y$). The substitution of the values thus found in the equation $y = ax^b$ gives a best power fit to the data.

A test of the applicability of a power function can be made quickly by the use of logarithmic coordinate paper. Logarithmic coordinate paper has its horizontal and vertical rulings placed at distances log 2, log 3, log 4, and so on, from the origin. The original data plotted on this kind of paper are equivalent to plotting the logarithms on the usual coordinate paper. The following example illustrates the method for the power function and the use of the special coordinate paper.

EXAMPLE. The relation between the pressure p and the volume V of a confined gas is given by

$$p = aV^b,$$

when the gas neither receives nor loses heat. Determine a and b for the data contained in the table.

V (cu ft)	9.80	6.72	4.53	4.16	3.36	2.83
p (lb/in²)	3	6	9	12	15	18

Solution. The given data are plotted on logarithmic paper in Fig. 8–3. The points are approximately in a straight line, and therefore indicate that an equation of the power type is suitable for representing the data.

We now replace each value in the table by its common logarithm.

$\log V$	.9912	.8274	.6561	.6191	.5263	.4518
$\log p$	.4771	.7782	.9542	1.0792	1.1761	1.2553

The equation corresponding to this transformed data is

$$\log p = b \log V + \log a.$$

To obtain the best linear fit to the new data, we employ formulas (1), using $\log V$ for x and $\log p$ for y. The first of the formulas yields the coefficient of $\log V$ and

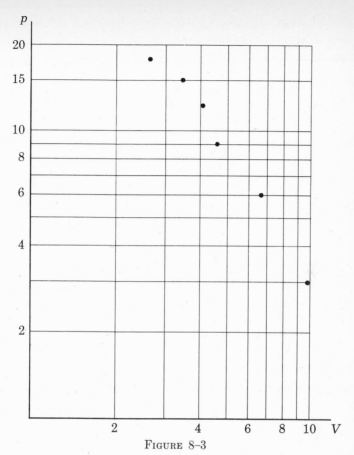

FIGURE 8–3

the second the constant term $\log a$.   We have the following sums:

$$\Sigma \log V = 4.0719, \qquad \Sigma(\log V)^2 = 2.9619,$$
$$\Sigma \log p = 5.7201, \quad \Sigma(\log V)(\log p) = 3.5971.$$

Substituting these values and $n = 6$, we get

$$b = \frac{6(3.5971) - 4.0719(5.7201)}{6(2.9619) - (4.0719)^2} = -1.43,$$

$$\log a = \frac{2.9620(5.7201) - 4.0719(3.5961)}{6(2.9619) - (4.0719)^2} = 1.9272,$$

$$a = 84.6.$$

Making these substitutions for a and b, we have

$$p = 84.6 \cdot V^{-1.43}$$

The graph of this equation and the points representing the original data are shown in Fig. 8–4.

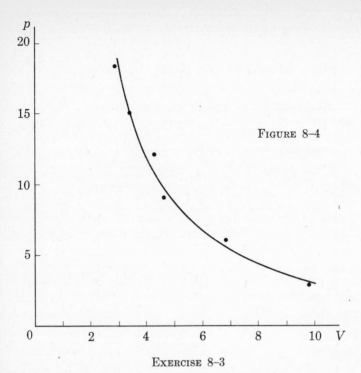

FIGURE 8–4

EXERCISE 8–3

In problems 1 and 2 assume the form $y = ax^b$ and determine a and b for the best fit.

1.

x	2	3	5	7
y	1	4	20	50

2.

x	1	2	3	4
	0.5	3.0	6.8	10.0

3. A body falls s feet in t seconds. Show that the form $t = as^b$ is applicable to the recorded data and determine a and b for the best fit.

s	4	10	16	25	36
t	.51	.79	1.01	1.24	1.49

4. If R is the air resistance in pounds against an automobile traveling at V miles per hour, show that the form $R = aV^b$ is applicable to the measurements in the table and find a and b for the best fit.

V	10	20	30	40	50
R	7	24	65	120	180

5. Corresponding measurements of the volume and pressure of steam are given in the table. Find the best fit of the form $p = aV^n$ to these data.

V	9	5	2.4	2.1	1
p	5	10	30	40	100

8–6 The exponential and logarithmic formulas. We saw in the preceding section that the power form can be reduced to a linear form. Similarly, the exponential and logarithmic forms are reducible to linear forms.

By taking the common logarithms of both members the equation

$$y = a \cdot 10^{bx}$$

becomes $\qquad\qquad \log y = bx + \log a.$

Here $\log y$ is a linear function of x. Hence the exponential formula is applicable to a set of data if the points $(x, \log y)$ are in close proximity to a straight line. Where this is the case, the procedure is to determine a and b so that $bx + \log a$ is the best linear fit to the set of points $(x, \log y)$.

To determine if the exponential function is adequate to represent the given data, semilogarithmic paper may be used. This paper has the usual scale along the x-axis, and the scale along the positive y-axis is logarithmic.

The equation $\qquad\qquad y = a \log x + b$

expresses y as a linear function of $\log x$. Here we would consider the points $(\log x, y)$. If these are about in a straight line, then a and b should be found for a linear fit to the points. The values thus obtained should be substituted in the logarithmic equation.

EXAMPLE. The number of bacteria N per unit volume in a culture after t hours is given by the table for several values of t. Show that $N = a \cdot 10^{bt}$ may represent the data and find values for a and b.

t	1	2	3	4	5
N	70	88	111	127	160

Solution. The given data, plotted on semilogarithmic paper, yield points almost collinear (Fig. 8–5). This indicates that the data can be approximated by an exponential formula. Hence we transform the given data by taking the logarithm of each N.

t	1	2	3	4	5
$\log N$	1.845	1.945	2.045	2.104	2.204

We compute the following sums:

$$\Sigma t = 15, \qquad\qquad \Sigma t^2 = 55,$$
$$\Sigma \log N = 10.143, \quad \Sigma t(\log N) = 31.306.$$

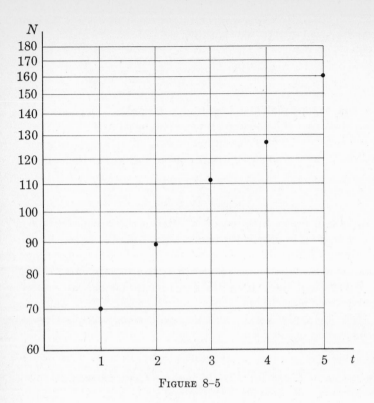

FIGURE 8–5

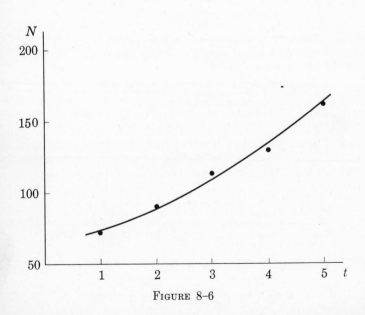

FIGURE 8–6

Using these values in formulas (1), we get

$$b = \frac{5(31.306) - 15(10.143)}{5(55) - 15^2} = \frac{4.385}{50} = 0.0877,$$

$$\log a = \frac{55(10.143) - 15(31.306)}{50} = 1.766,$$

$$a = 58.3.$$

We obtain the equation $N = 58.3 \cdot 10^{0.0877t}$. The graph and the given data are shown in Fig. 8–6.

Exercise 8–4

In problems 1–3 find best fits of the type indicated.

1.

x	-3	-1	1	3	5
y	0.8	1.5	2.7	4.9	9.0

$y = a \cdot 10^{bx}$

2.

x	0	1	2	3	5
y	3.0	2.5	2.1	1.6	1.1

$y = a \cdot 10^{bx}$

3.

x	$\frac{1}{2}$	1	3	5	8
y	0	3.1	7.8	9.9	12

$y = a \log x + b$

4. The bacteria count N per unit volume in a certain culture at the end of t hours was estimated as in the table. Find the best relation of the form $N = a \cdot 10^{bt}$.

t	0	2	4	6	8
N	10	16	25	40	63

5. The temperature T (degrees C) of a cooling body at time t (min) was measured as recorded. Find an exponential formula of best fit for T in terms of t.

t	0	1	2	3	4	5
T	100	79	63	50	40	32

6. The atmospheric pressure p in pounds per square inch at a height h in thousands of feet is shown in the table. Express p exponentially in terms of h.

h	0	5	10	15	20
p	14.6	12.1	10.1	8.4	7.0

7. The horsepower P required for the speeds V in knots for a certain ship are recorded in the table. Find the best fit to the data of the form $V = a \log P + b$.

P	2000	4000	7000	12000
V	12	13	14	15

CHAPTER 9

POLAR COORDINATES

9–1 Introduction. There are various types of coordinate systems. The rectangular system with which we have been dealing is probably the most important. In it a point is located by its distances from two perpendicular lines. We shall introduce in this chapter a coordinate system in which the coordinates of a point in a plane are its distance from a fixed point and its direction from a fixed line. The coordinates given in this way are called *polar coordinates*. The proper choice of a coordinate system depends on the nature of the problem at hand. For some problems either the rectangular or the polar system may be satisfactory; usually, however, one of the two is preferable. And in some situations it is advantageous to use both systems, shifting from one to the other.

9–2 The polar coordinate system. The reference frame in the polar coordinate system is a half-line drawn from some point in the plane. In Fig. 9–1 a half-line is represented by OA. The point O is called the *origin* or *pole* and OA is the *polar axis*. The position of any point P in the plane is definitely determined by the distance OP and the angle AOP. The segment OP, denoted by ρ, is referred to as the *radius vector;* the angle AOP, denoted by θ, is called the *vectorial angle*. The coordinates of P are then written as (ρ, θ).

It is customary to regard polar coordinates as signed quantities. The vectorial angle, as in trigonometry, is defined as positive or negative according as it is measured counterclockwise or clockwise from the polar axis. The ρ-coordinate is defined as positive if measured from the pole along the terminal side of θ and negative if measured along the terminal side extended through the pole.

A given pair of polar coordinates definitely locates a point. For example, the coordinates $(2, 30°)$ determine one particular point. To plot the point, we first draw the terminal side of a 30° angle measured counterclockwise from OA (Fig. 9–2) and then lay off two units along the terminal side. While this pair of coordinates defines a particular point, there are other coordinate values which define this same point. This is evident, since the vectorial angle may have 360° added or subtracted repeatedly without changing the point represented. Additional coordinates of the point may be had also by using a negative value for the distance coordinate. Restricting the vectorial angles to values numerically less than

120

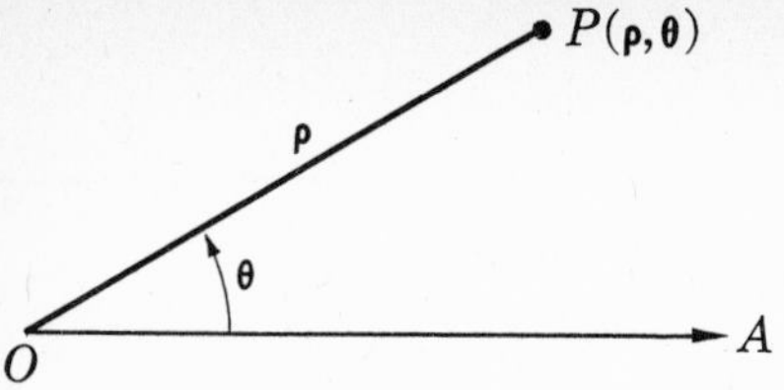

FIGURE 9–1

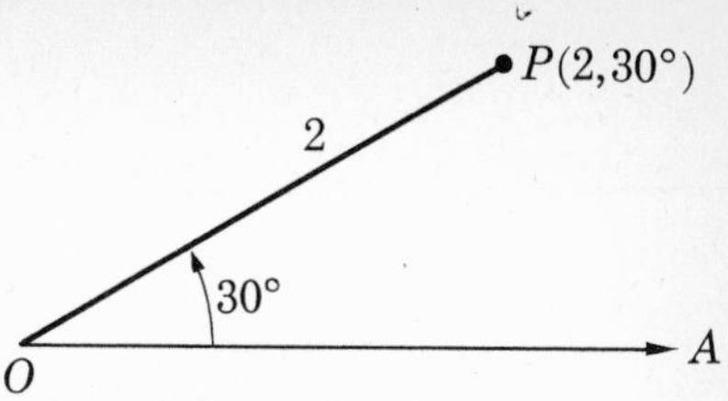

FIGURE 9–2

360°, the following coordinates define the same point:

$$(2,30°), \quad (2,-330°), \quad (-2,210°), \quad (-2,-150°).$$

The coordinates of the origin are $(0,\theta)$, where θ may be any angle.

The plotting of points in polar coordinates can be done more accurately by the use of polar coordinate paper. This paper has concentric circles and equally spaced radial lines through the center. For many purposes, however, sufficient accuracy is obtained by estimating the angles and distances by sight.

EXERCISE 9–1

1. Plot the points: $(3,60°)$, $(6,-30°)$, $(2,180°)$, $(-3,-225°)$, $(0,10°)$. Give three other sets of coordinates for each of the points, restricting the vectorial angles to values not exceeding 360° numerically.

2. Plot the points: $(5,210°)$, $(4,0°)$, $(-6,135°)$, $(-2,-180°)$. Give three other sets of coordinates for each of the points, where the numerical values of the vectorial angles do not exceed 360°.

3. Where are the points for which (a) $\rho = 4$, (b) $\rho = -4$, (c) $\theta = 45°$, (d) $\theta = -90°$?

4. Where are the points for which (a) $\rho = 0$, (b) $\theta = 0°$, (c) $\theta = \pi$?

9–3 Relations between rectangular and polar coordinates. As we have mentioned, it is often advantageous in the course of a problem to shift from one coordinate system to another. For this purpose we shall derive transformation formulas which express polar coordinates in terms of rectangular coordinates, and vice versa. In Fig. 9–3 the two systems are placed so that the origins coincide and the polar axis lies along the positive x-axis. Then a point P has the coordinates (x,y) and (ρ,θ). Noticing the triangle OMP, we have

$$\cos \theta = \frac{x}{\rho} \quad \text{and} \quad \sin \theta = \frac{y}{\rho},$$

and hence

$$x = \rho \cos \theta, \tag{1}$$
$$y = \rho \sin \theta. \tag{2}$$

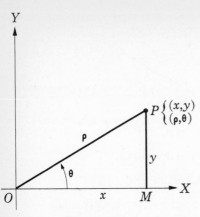

FIGURE 9–3

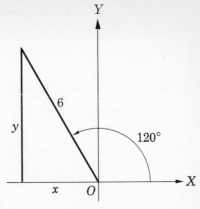

FIGURE 9–4

To obtain ρ and θ in terms of x and y, we write

$$\rho^2 = x^2 + y^2 \qquad \text{and} \qquad \tan \theta = \frac{y}{x}.$$

Whence, solving for ρ and θ,

$$\rho = \sqrt{x^2 + y^2}, \qquad (3)$$

$$\theta = \text{arc} \tan \frac{y}{x}. \qquad (4)$$

These four formulas enable us to transform the coordinates of a point, and therefore the equation of a locus, from one system to the other. The θ-coordinate as given by formula (4) is not single-valued. Hence it is necessary to select a proper value for θ when applying the formula to find this coordinate of a point. This is illustrated in Example 2.

EXAMPLE 1. Find the rectangular coordinates of the point defined by the polar coordinates (6,120°). (See Fig. 9–4.)

Solution. Using the formulas (1) and (2), we have

$$x = \rho \cos \theta = 6 \cos 120° = -3,$$
$$y = \rho \sin \theta = 6 \sin 120° = 3\sqrt{3}.$$

The required coordinates are $(-3, 3\sqrt{3})$.

EXAMPLE 2. Express the rectangular coordinates $(-2, -2)$ in terms of polar coordinates.

Solution. Here the formulas (3) and (4) give

$$\rho = \sqrt{x^2 + y^2} = 2\sqrt{2} \qquad \text{and} \qquad \theta = \text{arc} \tan \frac{y}{x} = \text{arc} \tan 1.$$

Since the point is in the third quadrant, we select $\theta = 225°$. Hence the pair of coordinates $(2\sqrt{2}, 225°)$ is a polar representation of the given point.

EXAMPLE 3.   Find the polar coordinate equation corresponding to $2x - 3y = 5$.

Solution.   Substituting for x and y gives

$$2(\rho \cos \theta) - 3(\rho \sin \theta) = 5 \qquad \text{or} \qquad \rho(2 \cos \theta - 3 \sin \theta) = 5.$$

EXAMPLE 4.   Transform the equation $\rho = 4 \sin \theta$ to rectangular coordinates.

Solution.   Since $\rho = \sqrt{x^2 + y^2}$ and $\sin \theta = \dfrac{y}{\rho} = \dfrac{y}{\sqrt{x^2 + y^2}}$, we substitute in the given equation and get

$$\sqrt{x^2 + y^2} = \frac{4y}{\sqrt{x^2 + y^2}},$$

or

$$x^2 + y^2 = 4y.$$

The required equation is seen to represent a circle.

EXERCISE 9–2

Find the rectangular coordinates of the following points.

1. $(4, 90°)$.
2. $(3\sqrt{2}, 45°)$.
3. $(7, 0°)$.
4. $(0, 180°)$.
5. $(-8, 270°)$.
6. $(-1, -60°)$.
7. $(6, 150°)$.
8. $(4\sqrt{2}, -135°)$.
9. $(9, 180°)$.

Find non-negative polar coordinates of the following points.

10. $(0, 3)$.
11. $(3, 0)$.
12. $(0, 0)$.
13. $(-1, 0)$.
14. $(0, -5)$.
15. $(\sqrt{2}, \sqrt{2})$.
16. $(6\sqrt{3}, -6)$.
17. $(-2\sqrt{3}, 2)$.
18. $(3, -4)$.
19. $(-4, 3)$.
20. $(5, 12)$.
21. $(-5, -12)$.

Transform the following equations into the corresponding polar coordinate equations.

22. $x = 3$.
23. $y = -4$
24. $2x - y = 3$.
25. $3x + y = 0$.
26. $y = x$.
27. $Ax + By = D$.
28. $x^2 + y^2 = 16$.
29. $xy = a^2$.
30. $x^2 + y^2 - 2x + 2y = 0$.
31. $x^2 - y^2 = a^2$.
32. $y^2 = 4x$.
33. $(x^2 + y^2)^2 = 2a^2xy$.

Transform the following equations to the corresponding rectangular coordinate equations.

34. $\rho = 4$.
35. $\theta = 0°$.
36. $\theta = 45°$.
37. $\rho = 2 \sin \theta + 2 \cos \theta$.
38. $\rho = 6 \sin \theta - 4 \cos \theta$
39. $\rho = 8 \cos \theta$.
40. $\rho = 8 \sin \theta$.
41. $\rho \cos \theta = 6$.
42. $\rho \sin \theta = 6$.
43. $\rho^2 \cos 2\theta = a^2$.
44. $\rho^2 \sin 2\theta = a^2$.
45. $\rho = \dfrac{3}{1 + \cos \theta}$.
46. $\rho = \dfrac{3}{2 + \cos \theta}$.

47. $\rho = \dfrac{2}{1 - 2\cos\theta}.$ 48. $\rho = \dfrac{2}{3\sin\theta + 4\cos\theta}.$

49. $\rho = \dfrac{5}{2\sin\theta - \cos\theta}.$

9–4 Graphs of polar coordinate equations. The definition of a graph in polar coordinates and the technique of its construction are essentially the same as that of an equation in rectangular coordinates.

DEFINITION. *The graph of an equation in polar coordinates consists of all the points which have coordinates satisfying the equation.*

We shall first consider comparatively simple equations and obtain their graphs by preparing tables of corresponding values of the variables. Later we shall discuss certain aids by which the curve tracing can be facilitated.

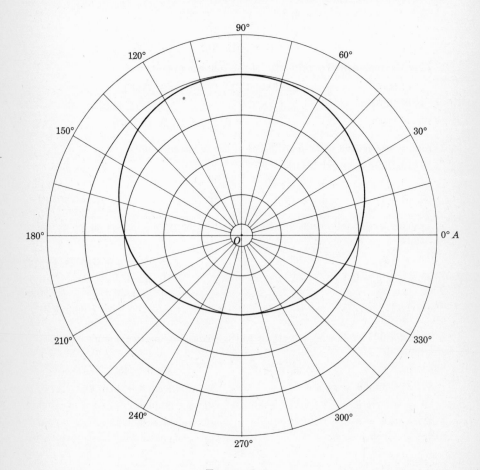

FIGURE 9–5

EXAMPLE 1.　Draw the graph of $\rho = 3 + \sin \theta$.

Solution.　We assign certain values to θ in the interval 0° to 360° and prepare the following table.

θ	0°	30°	45°	60°	90°	120°	150°	180°
ρ	3	3.5	3.7	3.9	4	3.9	3.5	3

θ	210°	225°	240°	270°	300°	315°	330°	360°
ρ	2.5	2.3	2.1	2	2.1	2.3	2.5	3

By plotting these points and drawing a curve through them the graph of Fig. 9–5 is obtained.

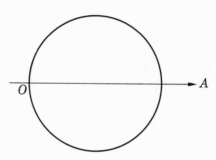

FIGURE 9–6

EXAMPLE 2.　Draw the graph of $\rho = 4 \cos \theta$.

Solution.　We first prepare a table of corresponding values of ρ and θ.

θ	0°	30°	45°	60°	75°	90°	120°	135°	150°	180°
ρ	4	3.5	2.8	2.0	1.0	0	−2.0	−2.8	−3.5	−4

This table yields the graph in Fig. 9–6. We did not extend the table to include values of θ in the interval 180° to 360°, since values of θ in this range would merely repeat the graph already obtained. For example, the point $(-3.5, 210°)$ is on the graph, but this point is also defined by the coordinates $(3.5, 30°)$.

The graph appears to be a circle. This surmise is verified by transforming the equation to rectangular coordinates. The transformed equation is $(x - 2)^2 + y^2 = 4$.

EXERCISE 9–3

Draw the graphs of the following equations. In the equations involving trigonometric functions, points plotted at 30° intervals will suffice, with a few exceptions.

1. $\rho = 5$.
2. $\rho = -5$.
3. $\theta = 120°$.
4. $\theta = 180°$.
5. $\rho = 1 - \cos \theta$.
6. $\rho = 1 - \sin \theta$.

7. $\rho = 2 + \cos \theta$.

8. $\rho = 2 - \sin \theta$.

9. $\rho = 10 \sin \theta$.

10. $\rho = 2a \cos \theta$.

11. $\rho = \tan \theta$.

12. $\rho = \sec \theta$.

13. $\rho = \dfrac{10}{2 + \sin \theta}$.

14. $\rho = \dfrac{8}{2 - \cos \theta}$.

15. $\rho = \dfrac{1}{1 + \cos \theta}$.

16. $\rho = \dfrac{1}{1 - \sin \theta}$.

17. $\rho = \dfrac{1}{1 - 2 \sin \theta}$.

18. $\rho = \dfrac{1}{1 + 2 \sin \theta}$.

19. $\rho = 10 \sin^2 \theta$.

20. $\rho = 10 \cos^2 \theta$.

21. $\rho = 10 \sec^2 \theta$.

22. $\rho = 4 \sin \theta - 4 \cos \theta$.

23. $\rho = 8 \sin \theta + 6 \cos \theta$.

9–5 Equations of lines and conics in polar coordinate forms. The equations of lines and conics can be obtained in polar coordinates by transforming the rectangular coordinate equations of these loci. The equations can also be derived directly. We shall derive the polar coordinate equation of a line in general position and the equations of the conic sections in special positions.

In Fig. 9–7 the segment OR is drawn perpendicular to the line L. We denote the length of this segment by p and the angle which it makes with the polar axis by ω. The coordinates of a variable point on the line are (ρ,θ). From the right triangle ORP, we have

$$\frac{p}{\rho} = \cos (\theta - \omega)$$

or

$$\rho \cos (\theta - \omega) = p. \qquad \textbf{(5)}$$

This equation holds for all points of the line. If P is chosen below OA, then the angle ROP is equal to $(\omega + 2\pi - \theta)$. Although this angle is not equal to $(\theta - \omega)$, we do have $\cos (\omega + 2\pi - \theta) = \cos (\omega - \theta) = \cos (\theta - \omega)$. In a similar way, the equation could be derived for the line L in any other position and not passing through the origin.

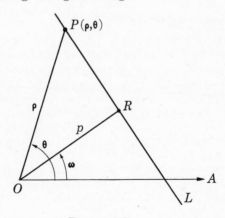

FIGURE 9–7

Formula (5) is called the *polar normal form* of the equation of a straight line. For lines perpendicular to the polar axis $\omega = 0°$ or $180°$, and for lines parallel to the polar axis $\omega = 90°$ or $270°$. Substituting these values for ω, we have the special forms

$$\rho \cos \theta = \pm p \tag{6}$$

and

$$\rho \sin \theta = \pm p. \tag{7}$$

The θ-coordinate is constant for points on a line passing through the origin. Hence the equation of a line through the origin with inclination α is

$$\theta = \alpha. \tag{8}$$

Although the equation of a line through the origin can be written immediately in this form, it is worth noting that equation (8) is a special case of equation (5). By setting $p = 0$ in equation (8), we have $\rho \cos (\theta - \omega) = 0$, $\cos (\theta - \omega) = 0$, $\theta - \omega = \frac{1}{2}\pi$, and $\theta = \frac{1}{2}\pi + \omega = \alpha$.

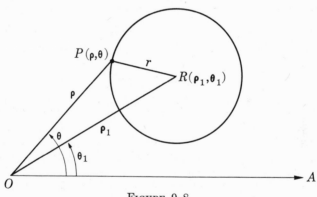

FIGURE 9–8

We next write the equation of a circle of radius r with center at (ρ_1, θ_1). Noticing Fig. 9–8 and applying the law of cosines to the triangle ORP, we get the equation of the circle in the form

$$\rho^2 + \rho_1{}^2 - 2\rho\rho_1 \cos (\theta - \theta_1) = r^2. \tag{9}$$

If the center is at $(r, 0°)$, then $\rho_1 = r$ and $\theta_1 = 0°$ and the equation reduces to

$$\rho = 2r \cos \theta. \tag{10}$$

If the center is at $(r, 90°)$, the equation becomes

$$\rho = 2r \sin \theta. \tag{11}$$

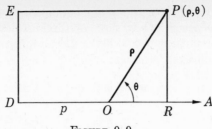

FIGURE 9-9

We use the focus-directrix property of conics (Exercise 8–1, problem 15) to derive their equations in polar coordinates. The equations can be obtained in simple forms if the focus and origin coincide and the directrix is parallel or perpendicular to the polar axis. In Fig. 9–9 the directrix DE is perpendicular to the polar axis and to the left of O. If we indicate the eccentricity by e, and the length of DO by p, we have for any point $P(\rho,\theta)$ of the conic

$$\frac{OP}{EP} = e.$$

But the numerator $OP = \rho$, and the denominator $EP = DR = DO + OR = p + \rho \cos \theta$. Hence $\rho/(p + \rho \cos \theta) = e$, and solving for ρ, we get

$$\rho = \frac{ep}{1 - e \cos \theta}. \tag{12}$$

When the focus is at the pole and the directrix is p units to the right of the pole, the equation is

$$\rho = \frac{ep}{1 + e \cos \theta}. \tag{13}$$

If the focus is at the pole and the directrix is parallel to the polar axis, the equation is

$$\rho = \frac{ep}{1 + e \sin \theta} \tag{14}$$

or

$$\rho = \frac{ep}{1 - e \sin \theta}, \tag{15}$$

depending on whether the directrix is p units above or below the pole.

An equation in any of the forms (12)–(15) represents a parabola if $e = 1$, an ellipse if e is between 0 and 1, and a hyperbola if e is greater than 1. The graph in any case can be sketched immediately. Having observed the type of conic from the value of e, the next step is to find the points where the curve cuts the polar axis, the extension of the axis through O, and the line through the pole perpendicular to the polar axis. These are called the *intercept points*, and may be obtained by using the values 0°, 90°, 180°, and 270° for θ. Only three of these values can be used for a parabola, since one of them would make a denominator zero. The intercept points are sufficient for a rough graph. For increased accuracy a few additional points should be plotted.

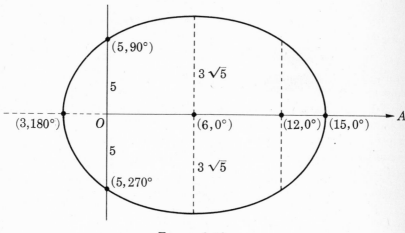

FIGURE 9–10

EXAMPLE. Sketch the graph of $\rho = 15/(3 - 2 \cos \theta)$.

Solution. The equation takes the form (12) when the numerator and denominator of the right member are divided by 3. This gives

$$\rho = \frac{5}{1 - (2/3) \cos \theta}.$$

In this form we observe that $e = 2/3$, and hence the graph is an ellipse. Substituting 0°, 90°, 180°, and 270° in succession for θ in the original equation, the intercept points are found to be

$$(15,0°), \quad (5,90°), \quad (3,180°), \quad \text{and} \quad (5,270°).$$

These points are plotted in Fig. 9–10. The points $(15,0°)$ and $(3,180°)$ are vertices and the other intercept points are the ends of a latus rectum. The center, midway between the vertices, is at $(6,0°)$. The length of the major axis $2a = 18$, and $a = 9$. The distance between the center and the focus at O is $c = 6$. Hence $b^2 = a^2 - c^2 = 81 - 36 = 45$, and $b = 3\sqrt{5}$.

EXERCISE 9–4

1. By use of a figure find the equation of the line perpendicular to the polar axis and (a) 3 units to the right of the pole, (b) 3 units to the left of the pole. Compare your results with formula (6).

2. By use of a figure find the equation of the line parallel to the polar axis and (a) 3 units below the axis, (b) 3 units above the axis. Check your results with formula (7).

3. Show that formula (5) can be reduced to the form

$$\rho = \frac{C}{A \cos \theta + B \sin \theta}.$$

Plot two points and draw the line represented by each equation 4–6.

4. $\rho = \dfrac{1}{\cos \theta + 2 \sin \theta}$.

5. $\rho = \dfrac{4}{2 \cos \theta - \sin \theta}$.

6. $\rho = \dfrac{-3}{2 \cos \theta + 5 \sin \theta}$.

Give the coordinates of the center and the radius of each circle defined by equations 7–10.

7. $\rho = 8 \cos \theta$.

8. $\rho = 6 \sin \theta$.

9. $\rho = -10 \sin \theta$.

10. $\rho = -4 \cos \theta$.

11. Use formula (9) and write the equation of the circle of radius 2 and (a) with center at $(4,0°)$, (b) with center at $(4,90°)$, (c) with center at $(2,0°)$.

Sketch the conics defined by equations 12–23.

12. $\rho = \dfrac{4}{1 - \cos \theta}$.

13. $\rho = \dfrac{6}{1 + \sin \theta}$.

14. $\rho = \dfrac{9}{2 + 2 \cos \theta}$.

15. $\rho = \dfrac{10}{3 - 3 \sin \theta}$.

16. $\rho = \dfrac{12}{2 - \cos \theta}$.

17. $\rho = \dfrac{12}{2 + \sin \theta}$.

18. $\rho = \dfrac{16}{4 + 3 \cos \theta}$.

19. $\rho = \dfrac{15}{5 - 4 \sin \theta}$.

30. $\rho = \dfrac{8}{1 - 2 \cos \theta}$.

21. $\rho = \dfrac{10}{2 + 3 \cos \theta}$.

22. $\rho = \dfrac{15}{3 + 5 \sin \theta}$.

23. $\rho = \dfrac{18}{3 - 4 \sin \theta}$.

9–6 Aids in graphing polar coordinate equations.

We have seen that an examination of an equation in rectangular coordinates may reveal short-cuts to the construction of its graph. In the same way, certain features of a graph in polar coordinates are often discovered by an analysis of its equation. It is better, for economy of time, to wrest useful information from an equation and thus keep at a minimum the tedious point-by-point plotting in sketching a graph. We shall discuss and illustrate certain simple devices in polar curve tracing.

Variation of ρ with θ. Many equations are sufficiently simple so that the way in which ρ varies as θ increases is evident. Usually a range of θ-values from 0° to 360° yields the complete graph. However, we shall find exceptions to this rule. By observing the equation and letting θ increase through its range, the graph can be visualized. A rough sketch may then be made with a few pencil strokes. To illustrate this situation, we use the equation

$$\rho = 3(1 + \sin \theta).$$

By starting at $\theta = 0°$ and increasing the angle in 90° steps to 360°, it is a simple matter to see how ρ varies in each 90° interval. This variation is represented in the diagram. The graph (Fig. 9–11) is a heart-shaped curve called the *cardioid*.

As θ increases from	$\sin \theta$ varies from	ρ varies from
0° to 90°	0 to 1	3 to 6
90° to 180°	1 to 0	6 to 3
180° to 270°	0 to −1	3 to 0
270° to 360°	−1 to 0	0 to 3

Tangent lines at the origin. If ρ shrinks to zero as θ approaches and takes a fixed value θ_0, then the line $\theta = \theta_0$ is tangent to the curve at the origin. Intuitively, this statement seems correct; it can be proved. In

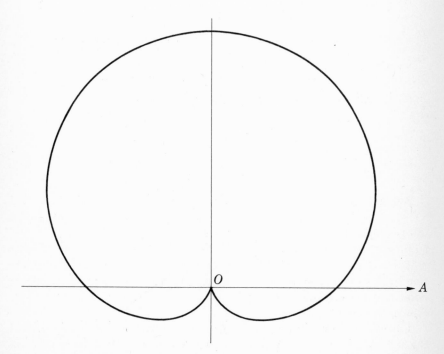

FIGURE 9–11

the preceding equation, $\rho = 3(1 + \sin \theta)$, the value of ρ diminishes to zero as θ increases to 270°. Hence the curve is tangent to the vertical line at the origin (Fig. 9–11).

To find the tangents to a curve at the origin, set $\rho = 0$ in the equation and solve for the corresponding values of θ.

Symmetry. We shall give tests for symmetry with respect to the pole, the polar axis, and the vertical line $\theta = 90°$. Noticing Fig. 9–12, the following tests are evident.

1. *If the equation is unchanged when ρ is replaced by $-\rho$ or when θ is replaced by 180° $+ \theta$, the graph is symmetric with respect to the pole.*

2. *If the equation is unchanged when θ is replaced by $-\theta$, the graph is symmetric with respect to the polar axis.*

3. *If the equation is unchanged when θ is replaced by 180° $- \theta$, the graph is symmetric with respect to the vertical line $\theta = 90°$.*

These tests will be found helpful. When any one is satisfied in an equation the symmetry is certain. On the other hand, the failure of a test does not disprove the symmetry in question. This is unlike the analogous situation in rectangular coordinates and is a consequence of the fact that a point has more than one polar coordinate representation. For example, replacing ρ by $-\rho$, the equation

$$\rho = \sin 2\theta \qquad \text{becomes} \qquad -\rho = \sin 2\theta.$$

This does not establish symmetry with respect to the pole. But substituting 180° $+ \theta$ for θ yields

$$\rho = \sin 2(180° + \theta) = \sin(360° + 2\theta) = \sin 2\theta,$$

which proves the symmetry with respect to the pole.

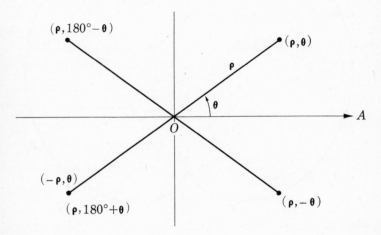

FIGURE 9–12

Continuing with the equation

$$\rho = \sin 2\theta,$$

we see that it does not satisfy tests 2 and 3. But it is sufficient to obtain the graph for θ from 0° to 180°, and then to complete the drawing by the known symmetry with respect to the pole. Since we have a trigonometric function of 2θ, it is convenient to consider the variation of ρ as θ increases in steps of 45°. The diagram indicates this variation. From it we see

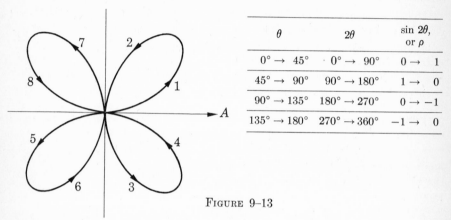

θ	2θ	$\sin 2\theta$, or ρ
0° → 45°	0° → 90°	0 → 1
45° → 90°	90° → 180°	1 → 0
90° → 135°	180° → 270°	0 → −1
135° → 180°	270° → 360°	−1 → 0

FIGURE 9–13

the values of θ corresponding to the zero value of ρ, and therefore conclude that the graph is tangent to the polar axis and the vertical line at the origin. Having completed the graph (Fig. 9–13), it is seen that it has all three types of symmetry. Because of its shape, the graph is called a *four-leaved rose*. The barbs and numbers indicate how a point would move in tracing the curve as θ increases from 0° to 360°.

Excluded values. Frequently equations are met in which certain values of the variables are excluded. For example, $\rho^2 = a^2 \sin \theta$ places restrictions on both ρ and θ. The values of ρ are in the range $-a$ to a, and θ cannot have a value between 180° and 360°, since ρ is imaginary for these values. The curve extends into the third and fourth quadrants, however, since the graph is symmetric with respect to the origin.

9–7 Special types of equations. There are several types of polar coordinate equations whose graphs have been given special names. We consider a few of these equations.

The graphs of equations of the forms

$$\rho = a \sin n\theta \qquad \text{and} \qquad \rho = a \cos n\theta,$$

where n is a positive integer, are called *rose curves*. The graph of a rose curve consists of equally spaced closed loops extending from the origin.

The number of loops, or leaves, depends on the integer n. If n is odd, there are n leaves; if n is even, there are $2n$ leaves. Figure 9–13 pictures a four-leaved rose.

The graph of an equation of the form

$$\rho = b + a \sin \theta$$

or

$$\rho = b + a \cos \theta$$

is called a *limaçon*. The shape of the graph depends on the relative values of a and b. If $a = b$, the limaçon is called a cardioid from its heart-like shape, as illustrated in Fig. 9–11. If the numerical value of b is greater than that of a, the graph is a curve surrounding the origin (Fig. 9–5). An interesting feature is introduced in the graph when a is numerically greater than b. The curve then has an inner loop. To show this, we draw the graph of

$$\rho = 2 + 4 \cos \theta.$$

Replacing θ by $-\theta$ leaves the equation unchanged, since $\cos (-\theta) = \cos \theta$. Hence there is symmetry with respect to the polar axis. Setting $\rho = 0$ gives

$$2 + 4 \cos \theta = 0,$$
$$\cos \theta = -\tfrac{1}{2},$$
$$\theta = 120°, 240°.$$

The lines $\theta = 120°$ and $\theta = 240°$ are tangent to the curve at the origin. The diagram indicates the variation of ρ as θ increases from $0°$ to $180°$. The graph is shown in Fig. 9–14; the lower half of the large loop and the upper half of the small loop were drawn by the use of symmetry.

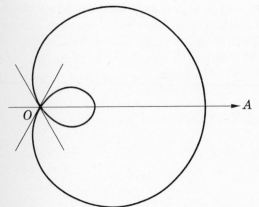

θ	$\cos \theta$	ρ
$0° \rightarrow 90°$	$1 \rightarrow 0$	$6 \rightarrow 2$
$90° \rightarrow 120°$	$0 \rightarrow -\tfrac{1}{2}$	$2 \rightarrow 0$
$120° \rightarrow 180°$	$-\tfrac{1}{2} \rightarrow -1$	$0 \rightarrow -2$

FIGURE 9–14

The graphs of the equations

$$\rho^2 = a^2 \sin 2\theta \qquad \text{and} \qquad \rho^2 = a^2 \cos 2\theta$$

are *lemniscates*.   In each of these equations ρ ranges from $-a$ to a and values of θ which make the right member negative are excluded.   In the first equation θ may not take a value between 90° and 180° or between 270° and 360°.   In the second the excluded intervals are $45° < \theta < 135°$ and $225° < \theta < 315°$.

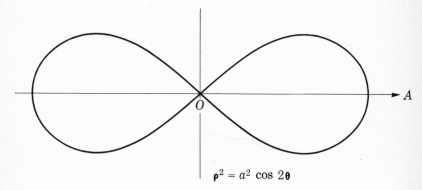

$$\rho^2 = a^2 \cos 2\theta$$

FIGURE 9–15

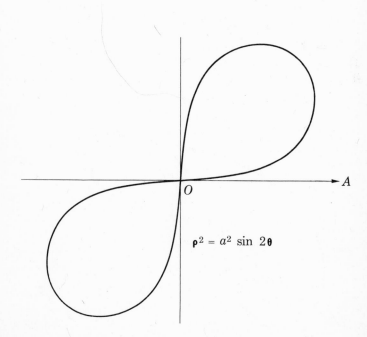

$$\rho^2 = a^2 \sin 2\theta$$

FIGURE 9–16

Discussing further the equation

$$\rho^2 = a^2 \cos 2\theta,$$

we observe that its graph is symmetric with respect to the pole, the polar axis, and the vertical line through the pole. As θ increases from 0° to 45°, the positive values of ρ vary from a to 0 and the negative values from $-a$ to 0. Hence this interval for θ gives rise to the upper half of the right loop and the lower half of the left loop of the graph (Fig. 9–15). Either of these half loops combined with the known symmetries is sufficient for completing the graph.

Finally, the equations

$$\rho = e^{a\theta}, \quad \rho\theta = a, \quad \text{and} \quad \rho = a\theta,$$

are examples of *spirals*. Their graphs for $a > 0$ and $\theta \geq 0°$ are shown in Figs. 9–17 to 9–19.

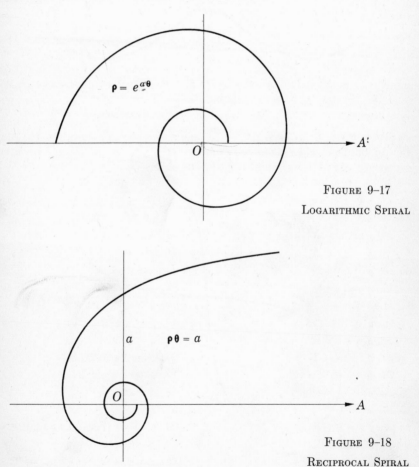

FIGURE 9–17

LOGARITHMIC SPIRAL

FIGURE 9–18

RECIPROCAL SPIRAL

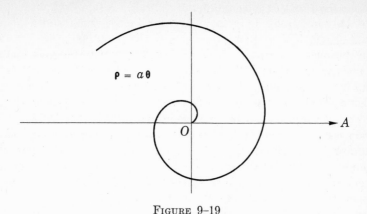

$$\rho = a\theta$$

FIGURE 9–19

SPIRAL OF ARCHIMEDES

EXERCISE 9–5

1. Observe that (ρ,θ) and $(-\rho,180° - \theta)$ are symmetric with respect to the polar axis, and that (ρ,θ) and $(-\rho,-\theta)$ are symmetric with respect to the line $\theta = 90°$. On the basis of this information, state two tests for the symmetry of the graph of an equation. Apply the tests to the equation $\rho = \sin 2\theta$.

Sketch the graph of each of the following equations. First examine the equation to find properties which are helpful in tracing the graph. Where the literal constant a occurs, assign to it a convenient positive value. In the spirals 25–29 use radian measure for θ.

2. $\rho = 4(1 - \cos \theta)$.   3. $\rho = 6(1 - \sin \theta)$.

4. $\rho = a(1 + \cos \theta)$.   5. $\rho = 5 - 2 \sin \theta$.

6. $\rho = 10 - 5 \cos \theta$.   7. $\rho = 8 + 4 \cos \theta$.

8. $\rho = 8 \cos 2\theta$.   9. $\rho = a \sin 2\theta$.

10. $\rho = 6 \sin 3\theta$.   11. $\rho = 4 \cos 3\theta$.

12. $\rho = 2 \sin 5\theta$.   13. $\rho = 2 \cos 5\theta$.

14. $\rho = 4 - 8 \cos \theta$.   15. $\rho = 6 - 3 \sin \theta$.

16. $\rho = 4 + 8 \cos \theta$.   17. $\rho = 6 + 3 \sin \theta$.

18. $\rho = a \cos 4\theta$.   19. $\rho = a \sin 4\theta$.

20. $\rho^2 = 9 \cos 2\theta$.   21. $\rho^2 = 16 \sin 2\theta$.

22. $\rho^2 = -a^2 \cos 2\theta$.   23. $\rho^2 = -a^2 \sin 2\theta$.

24. $\rho^2 = a^2 \cos \theta$.   25. $\rho = 2\theta$.

26. $\rho\theta = 4$.   27. $\rho = e^{\theta}$.

28. $\rho^2\theta = a$ (Lituus).   29. $\rho^2 = a^2\theta$ (Parabolic Spiral).

30. $\rho = \sin \frac{1}{2}\theta$.   31. $\rho = \cos \frac{1}{2}\theta$.

32. $\rho = 3 \sec \theta + 4$.   33. $\rho = 6 \sec \theta - 6$.

9–8 Intersections of polar coordinate curves. A simultaneous real solution of two equations in rectangular coordinates represents a point of intersection of their graphs. Conversely, the coordinates of a point of intersection yield a simultaneous solution. In polar coordinates, however, this converse statement does not always hold. This difference in the two systems is a consequence of the fact that a point has more than one pair of polar coordinates. As an illustration, consider the equations $\rho = -2$, $\rho = 1 + \sin\theta$ and the two pairs of coordinates $(2,90°)$, $(-2,270°)$. The equation $\rho = -2$ is satisfied by the second pair of coordinates but not by the first. The equation $\rho = 1 + \sin\theta$ is satisfied by the first pair of coordinates but not by the second. The two pairs of coordinates, however, determine the same point. Although the two curves pass through this point, no pair of coordinates of the point satisfies both equations. The usual process of solving two equations simultaneously does not yield an intersection point of this kind. The graphs of the equations, of course, show all intersections.

EXAMPLE 1. Solve simultaneously and sketch the graphs of

$$\rho = 6\sin\theta \qquad \text{and} \qquad \rho = 6\cos\theta.$$

Solution. Equating the right members of the equations, we have

$$6\sin\theta = 6\cos\theta,$$
$$\tan\theta = 1,$$
$$\theta = 45°, 225°,$$
$$\rho = 3\sqrt{2}, -3\sqrt{2}.$$

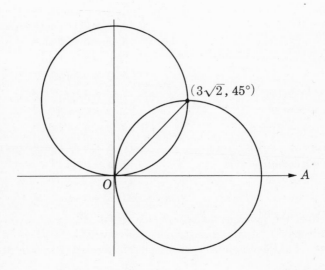

$(3\sqrt{2}, 45°)$

FIGURE 9–20

The coordinates $(3\sqrt{2},45°)$ and $(-3\sqrt{2},225°)$ define the same point.   The graphs (Fig. 9–20) show this point, and show also that both curves pass through the origin.   The coordinates $(0,0°)$ satisfy the first equation and $(0,90°)$ satisfy the second equation.   But the origin has no pair of coordinates which satisfies both equations.

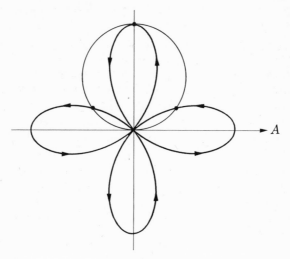

FIGURE 9–21

EXAMPLE 2.   Solve simultaneously and draw the graphs of

$$\rho = 4 \sin \theta \qquad \text{and} \qquad \rho = 4 \cos 2\theta.$$

Solution.   Eliminating ρ and using the trigonometric identity $\cos 2\theta = 1 - 2\sin^2 \theta$, we obtain

$$4 \sin \theta = 4(1 - 2 \sin^2 \theta),$$
$$2 \sin^2 \theta + \sin \theta - 1 = 0,$$
$$(2 \sin \theta - 1)(\sin \theta + 1) = 0,$$
$$\sin \theta = \tfrac{1}{2}, -1,$$
$$\theta = 30°, 150°, 270°,$$
$$\rho = 2, \quad 2, \quad -4.$$

The solutions are $(2,30°)$, $(2,150°)$, and $(-4,270°)$.   Figure 9–21 shows that the curves also cross at the origin, but the origin has no pair of coordinates which satisfies both equations.

EXERCISE 9–6

In each of the following problems solve the equations simultaneously and sketch their graphs.   Extraneous solutions are sometimes introduced in the solving process.   For this reason all results should be checked.

1. $\rho = 2 \cos \theta,$
    $\rho = 1.$

2. $\rho = 4 \sin \theta$
    $\rho = 2.$

3. $\rho = 6 \cos \theta$,
   $\rho \cos \theta = 3$.

4. $\rho = a(1 + \sin \theta)$,
   $\rho = 2a \sin \theta$.

5. $\rho = a(1 + \cos \theta)$,
   $\rho = a(1 - \cos \theta)$.

6. $\rho \cos \theta = 1$,
   $\rho = 2$.

7. $\rho^2 = 4 \cos \theta$,
   $\rho = 2$.

8. $\rho = 1 + \sin \theta$,
   $\rho = 1 + \cos \theta$.

9. $\rho = \dfrac{2}{1 + \cos \theta}$,
   $3\rho \cos \theta = 2$.

10. $\rho = \dfrac{3}{4 - 3 \cos \theta}$,
    $\rho = 3 \cos \theta$.

11. $\rho = 2 \sin \theta + 1$,
    $\rho = \cos \theta$.

12. $\rho^2 = a^2 \sin 2\theta$,
    $\rho = a\sqrt{2} \cos \theta$.

13. $\rho = 2 \sin \tfrac{1}{2}\theta$,
    $\theta = 60°$.

14. $\rho = \sin^2 \theta$,
    $\rho = \cos^2 \theta$.

15. $\rho = 2 \sin \tfrac{1}{2}\theta$,
    $\rho = 1$.

16. $\rho = 1 - \sin \theta$,
    $\rho = \cos 2\theta$.

17. $\rho = 4 + \cos \theta$,
    $\rho \cos \theta = -3$.

18. $\rho = 4 - \sin \theta$,
    $\rho \sin \theta = 3$.

19. $\rho = 2 \cos \theta + 1$,
    $\rho \cos \theta = 1$.

20. $\rho = \dfrac{2}{\sin \theta + \cos \theta}$,
    $\rho = \dfrac{2}{1 - \cos \theta}$.

CHAPTER 10

PARAMETRIC EQUATIONS

10–1 Introduction. Relations between x and y up to this point have been expressed by equations involving these variables. Another way of defining a relation between x and y is through the use of two equations in which each variable is expressed separately in terms of a third variable. The third variable is called a *parameter* and the equations are called *parametric equations*. Equations of this kind are of considerable importance; the mathematical treatment of many problems is facilitated by their use. The equations

$$x = 2t \qquad \text{and} \qquad y = t - 4,$$

for example, are parametric equations and t is the parameter. The equations define a locus. If a value is assigned to t, corresponding values are determined for x and y, which are the coordinates of a point of the locus. The complete locus consists of the points determined in this way as t varies through all its values. The relation between x and y is expressed directly by eliminating t between the two equations. Thus solving either of these equations for t and substituting in the other, we get

$$x - 2y = 8.$$

Often the parameter can be eliminated, as we have here done, to obtain a direct relation. Sometimes, however, this process is not easy or possible because the parameter is involved in a complicated way. The equations

$$x = t^5 + \log t \qquad \text{and} \qquad y = t^3 + \tan t$$

illustrate this statement.

It is sometimes helpful in the course of a problem to change an equation in x and y to parametric form. Consider, for example, the parabola defined by

$$x^2 + 2x + y = 4.$$

If we substitute $2t$ for x and solve the resulting equation for y, we get $y = 4 - 4t - 4t^2$. Hence the parametric equations

$$x = 2t \qquad \text{and} \qquad y = 4 - 4t - 4t^2$$

represent the parabola. It is evident that other representations could be obtained, since x may be equated to any function of t. This procedure is

141

inconvenient or perhaps impossible in equations which contain both variables in an involved way.

The parameter as here used plays a different role from the parameter which we discussed in Section 3–5. Here the parameter is a variable, and a curve is determined by letting the parameter vary through its range. In contrast, the parameter in a linear equation in x and y gives rise to a family of curves (lines). A line is determined by each value assigned to the parameter.

10–2 Parametric equations of the circle and ellipse. To find a parametric representation of the circle of radius a and center at the origin, we select for the parameter the angle θ indicated in Fig. 10–1. We have at once

$$x = a \cos \theta \qquad \text{and} \qquad y = a \sin \theta.$$

If we let θ increase from $0°$ to $360°$, the point (x,y), defined by these equations, starts at $(a,0)$ and moves counterclockwise around the circle. By letting θ change directly with the time t so that $\theta = kt$, the equations become

$$x = a \cos kt \qquad \text{and} \qquad y = a \sin kt.$$

These equations give the location of the moving point at any time. The speed of the point is constant.

The equations $x = a \cos \theta$ and $y = b \sin \theta$ represent an ellipse. This statement can be verified by eliminating the parameter θ. Writing the equations as

$$\frac{x}{a} = \cos \theta \qquad \text{and} \qquad \frac{y}{b} = \sin \theta,$$

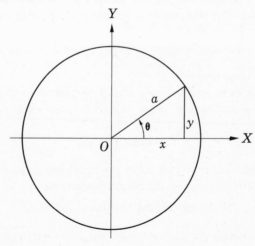

FIGURE 10–1

squaring both members of each equation, and adding, we get

$$\frac{x^2}{a^2} + \frac{y^2}{b^2} = 1.$$

From this result we see that the parametric equations represent an ellipse, and we are able to interpret the quantities a and b. The geometric significance of θ can be seen in Fig. 10–2. The concentric circles are of radii a and b. The terminal side of θ cuts the circles at A and B. The intersection of the vertical line through A and the horizontal line through B gives a point of the ellipse. For this point P, we have

$$x = OM = OA \cos \theta = a \cos \theta,$$
$$y = MP = NB = OB \sin \theta = b \sin \theta.$$

Hence as θ varies, P moves along an ellipse. The ellipse is traced by letting θ vary through 360°. If θ starts at 0° and increases to 360°, the point P starts at $(a,0)$ and traces the ellipse in a counterclockwise direction.

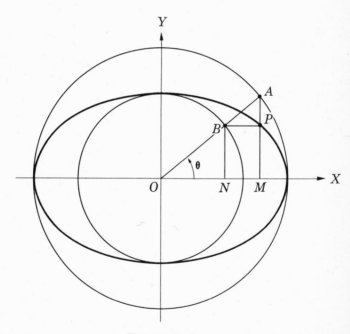

FIGURE 10-2

10–3 The graph of parametric equations. To obtain the graph of two parametric equations, we first assign to the parameter a set of values and compute the corresponding values of x and y. We then use the plotted points (x,y) for drawing the graph. An alternate procedure is to eliminate the parameter and construct the graph of the resulting equation. In some cases, however, the graph of the parametric equations is only a part of the graph of the rectangular equation. Example 2 illustrates this case.

EXAMPLE 1. Sketch the graph of

$$x = 5t - t^2 \quad \text{and} \quad y = 4t - t^2.$$

Solution. The table is the result of assigning to t the indicated values and finding the corresponding values of x and y. The graph (Fig. 10–3) is the curve drawn through the points (x,y) as determined by the table.

t	$-\frac{3}{2}$	-1	$-\frac{1}{2}$	0	$\frac{1}{2}$	1	$\frac{3}{2}$	2	$\frac{5}{2}$	3	$\frac{7}{2}$	4	$\frac{9}{2}$	5	$\frac{11}{2}$
x	$-\frac{39}{4}$	-6	$-\frac{11}{4}$	0	$\frac{9}{4}$	4	$\frac{21}{4}$	6	$\frac{25}{4}$	6	$\frac{21}{4}$	4	$\frac{9}{4}$	0	$-\frac{11}{4}$
y	$-\frac{33}{4}$	-5	$-\frac{9}{4}$	0	$\frac{7}{4}$	3	$\frac{15}{4}$	4	$\frac{15}{4}$	3	$\frac{7}{4}$	0	$-\frac{9}{4}$	-5	$-\frac{33}{4}$

To eliminate the parameter between the preceding equations we subtract the second equation from the first, which gives

$$x - y = t.$$

Then substituting $x - y$ for t in either of the given equations and simplifying, we obtain

$$x^2 - 2xy + y^2 - 4x + 5y = 0.$$

By the test of Section 5–13 the graph is a parabola. The graph is probably more easily obtained from the parametric equations than from the rectangular equation.

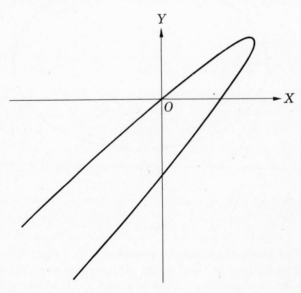

FIGURE 10–3

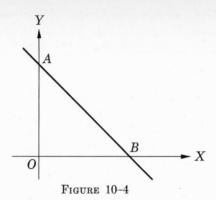

FIGURE 10–4

EXAMPLE 2. Construct the graph of

$$x = 2 \sin^2 \theta \qquad \text{and} \qquad y = 2 \cos^2 \theta.$$

Solution. The graph is more easily obtained from the direct relation. By adding the parametric equations, we obtain

$$x + y = 2(\sin^2 \theta + \cos^2 \theta)$$

or

$$x + y = 2.$$

The graph is the line in Fig. 10–4. We note, however, that the graph of the parametric equations is the segment AB. This results from the fact that the values of x and y are restricted to the range 0 to 2.

EXERCISE 10–1

Sketch the curve represented by each pair of equations 1–10. Check the graph by use of the rectangular equation obtained by eliminating the parameter.

1. $x = 2 - t, y = 3t.$
2. $x = t^2, y = 4t.$
3. $x = 6t^{-1}, y = t.$
4. $x = t, y = t^3.$
5. $x = 3t, y = 1 - t^2.$
6. $x = 5 \sin \theta, y = 5 \cos \theta.$
7. $x = 4 \cos \theta, y = 3 \sin \theta.$
8. $x = \cos 2\theta, y = 2 \sin \theta.$
9. $x = \dfrac{2}{1 + t^2}, y = \dfrac{2t}{1 + t^2}.$
10. $x = 2 + 5 \sin \theta, y = 2 - 3 \cos \theta.$

Eliminate the parameter from each pair of equations in problems 11–20. Sketch the curve, using either the parametric equations or the rectangular equation.

11. $x = 2 \sin \theta, y = \cos^2 \theta.$
12. $x = \tan^2 \theta, y = \sec^2 \theta.$
13. $x = \sec \theta, y = \tan \theta.$
14. $x = t^2 + 4t, y = t^2 + 3t.$
15. $x = t^{-1}, y = t - t^{-1}.$
16. $x = \sin \theta - \cos \theta, y = \sin \theta + \cos \theta.$
17. $x = \cos \theta, y = \cos \theta + \sin \theta.$
18. $x = t - 1, y = \dfrac{4t}{t - 3}.$

19. $x = \tan\theta - \cot\theta, y = \tan\theta + \cot\theta$.   20. $x = \sin\theta - \cos\theta, y = \sin\theta$.

Use radian measure for the parameter in each problem 21–26 and sketch the curve for t in the interval 0 to 2π.

21. $x = t + \sin t, y = \cos t$.   22. $x = t + \sin t, y = t + \cos t$.

23. $x = \frac{1}{10}e^t, y = \sin t$.   24. $x = 10e^{-t}, y = \sin t$.

25. $x = t \cos t, y = \sin t$.   26. $x = t \sin t, y = t \cos t$.

27. Show that

$$x = \frac{3t}{1 + t^3}, \quad y = \frac{3t^2}{1 + t^3}$$

yield $x^3 + y^3 - 3xy = 0$. Sketch the graph. Notice that the parametric equations are preferable for this purpose.

10–4 The path of a projectile. The equations of certain curves can be determined more readily by the use of a parameter than otherwise. In fact, this is one of the principal uses of parametric equations. In the remainder of this chapter parametric equations of curves are required. These curves have interesting properties and also have important practical and theoretical applications.

We consider first the path of a projectile in air. Suppose that a body is given an initial upward velocity of v_0 feet per second in a direction which makes an angle α with the horizontal. Assuming that the resistance of the air is small and can be neglected without great error, the object moves subject to the vertical force of gravity. This means that there is no horizontal force to change the speed in the horizontal direction. Noticing Fig. 10–5 with the origin of coordinates at the point where the projectile is fired, we see that the velocity in the x-direction is $v_0 \cos\alpha$. Then the distance traveled horizontally at the end of t seconds is $(v_0 \cos\alpha)t$ feet. Now the projectile is started with a vertical component of velocity of $v_0 \sin\alpha$ feet per second. This velocity would cause the projectile to rise upward to a height of $(v_0 \sin\alpha)t$ feet in t seconds. But the effect of the pull of gravity lessens this distance. According to a formula of physics

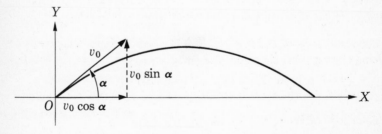

FIGURE 10–5

the amount to be subtracted is $\frac{1}{2}gt^2$, where g is a constant and approximately equal to 32.   Hence the parametric equations of the path are

$$x = (v_0 \cos \alpha)t, \quad y = (v_0 \sin \alpha)t - \tfrac{1}{2}gt^2. \tag{1}$$

If we solve the first equation for t and substitute the result in the second, we get the equation of the path in the rectangular form

$$y = (\tan \alpha)x - \frac{gx^2}{2v_0{}^2 \cos^2 \alpha}. \tag{2}$$

This equation, which is of the second degree in x and the first degree in y, represents a parabola.

EXAMPLE.   A stone is thrown upward with a velocity of 160 feet per second at an angle of 45° with the horizontal.   Write the equations of the path in parametric and rectangular forms.

Solution.   We substitute $v_0 = 160, \alpha = 45°$, and $g = 32$ in equations (1) and (2). This gives the parametric equations

$$x = 80\sqrt{2}t, \quad y = 80\sqrt{2}t - 16t^2,$$

and the rectangular equation

$$y = x - \frac{x^2}{800}.$$

This last equation, reduced to standard form, becomes

$$(x - 400)^2 = -800(y - 200).$$

The vertex, at (400,200), is the highest point reached by the stone.   Setting $y = 0$, we find $x = 800$.   Hence the stone strikes the ground at the point (800,0).

10–5 The cycloid.   The path traced by a given point on the circumference of a circle which rolls along a line is called a *cycloid*.   In order to derive the equation of the cycloid, we select the line as the x-axis and take the origin at a position where the tracing point is in contact with the x-axis.

In Fig. 10–6 the radius of the rolling circle is a, and P is the tracing point.   In the position drawn, the circle has rolled so that CP makes an angle θ (radians) with the vertical.   Having rolled without slipping, the segment OB and the arc PB are of equal length.   Hence

$$OB = \text{arc } PB = a\theta.$$

Noticing the right triangle PDC, we may write

$$x = OA = OB - PD = a\theta - a \sin \theta,$$
$$y = AP = BC - DC = a - a \cos \theta.$$

The equations of the cycloid in parametric form are

$$x = a(\theta - \sin \theta), \quad y = a(1 - \cos \theta).$$

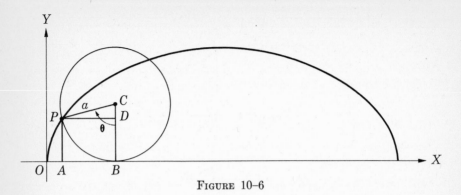

FIGURE 10–6

The result of eliminating θ from these equations is the complicated equation

$$x = a \text{ arc cos } \frac{a - y}{a} \pm \sqrt{2\,ay - y^2}.$$

EXERCISE 10–2

1. A ball is thrown upward with an initial velocity of 80 feet per second at an angle of 45° with the horizontal. Write the parametric equations of its path, using $g = 32$. Find also the rectangular equation of the path. How high does the ball ascend and how far away, assuming the ground level, does it strike the ground?

2. A projectile is fired upward with a velocity of 160 feet per second at an angle of 30° with the horizontal. Find the coordinates of its position at the end of (a) 1 second, (b) 3 seconds, (c) 5 seconds. At what times is the projectile 64 feet above the starting point?

3. Write the equations, both in parametric and rectangular forms, of the path of a projectile which is fired horizontally with a velocity of v_0 feet per second. If the projectile is fired horizontally from a building 64 feet high, find how far downward and how far horizontally it travels in 2 seconds.

4. A circle of radius a rolls along a line. A point on a radius, b units from the center, describes a path. Paralleling the derivation in Section 10–5, show that the path is represented by the equations

$$x = a\theta - b \sin \theta, \quad y = a - b \cos \theta$$

The curve is called a *curtate cycloid* if $b < a$ and a *prolate cycloid* if $b > a$.

5. Sketch the curve of the equations in problem 4, taking $a = 4$ and $b = 3$. Sketch the curve if $a = 4$ and $b = 6$.

6. A circle of radius 4 rolls along a line and makes a revolution in 2 seconds. A point, starting downward on a vertical radius, moves from the center to the circumference along the radius at a rate of 2 feet per second. Find the equations of the path of the point.

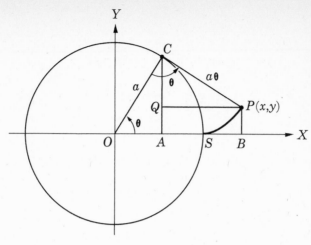

FIGURE 10–7

7. The end of a thread, kept in the plane of a circle, as it is unwound tautly from the circle describes a path called the *involute* of the circle. Use Fig. 10–7 to show that the parametric equations of the involute are

$$x = a(\cos \theta + \theta \sin \theta), \quad y = a(\sin \theta - \theta \cos \theta).$$

8. In Fig. 10–8 a circle of radius a is tangent to the two parallel lines OX and AC. The line OC cuts the circle at B, and $P(x,y)$ is the intersection of a horizontal line through B and a vertical line through C. Show that the equations of the locus of P, as C moves along the upper tangent, are

$$x = 2a \tan \theta, \quad y = 2a \cos^2 \theta.$$

This curve is called the *witch of Agnesi*. Show that its rectangular equation is

$$y = \frac{8a^3}{x^2 + 4a^2}.$$

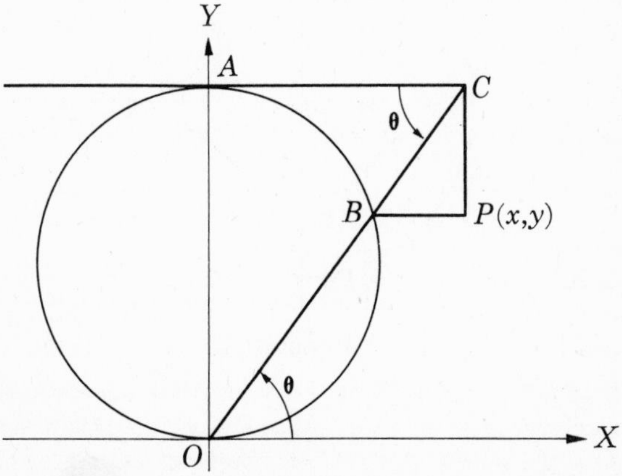

FIGURE 10–8

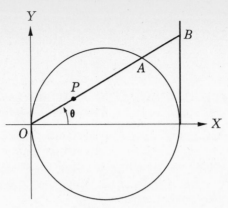

FIGURE 10–9

9. In Fig. 10–9, $OP = AB$. Show that the equations of the path traced by P, as A moves around the circle, are

$$x = 2a \sin^2 \theta, \quad y = 2a \sin^2 \theta \tan \theta.$$

The curve is called the *cissoid of Diocles*. The rectangular equation is

$$y^2 = \frac{x^3}{2a - x}.$$

10. The path traced by a given point on the circumference of a circle of radius $\frac{1}{4}a$ as it rolls inside and along a circle of radius a is called a *hypocycloid of four cusps*. Use Fig. 10–10 to obtain the parametric equations

$$x = a \cos^3 \theta, \quad y = a \sin^3 \theta.$$

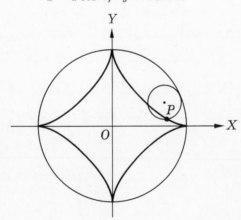

FIGURE 10–10

CHAPTER 11

SPACE COORDINATES AND SURFACES

11–1 Space coordinates. In our study thus far we have dealt with equations in two variables, and have pictured equations in a plane coordinate system. When we introduce a third variable a plane will not suffice for the illustration of an equation. For this purpose our coordinate system is extended to three dimensions.

Let OX, OY, and OZ be three mutually perpendicular lines. These lines constitute the x-axis, the y-axis, and the z-axis. The positive directions of the axes are indicated by arrows in Fig. 11–1. In this drawing, and others which we shall make, the x- and z-axes are in the plane of the page, and the y-axis is to be visualized as perpendicular to the page. The z-axis may be regarded as vertical and the others as horizontal. The axes, in pairs, determine the three mutually perpendicular planes, XOY, XOZ, and YOZ. These are called *coordinate planes*, and are designated respectively the xy-plane, the xz-plane, and the yz-plane. The coordinate planes divide space into eight regions, called *octants*. The octant with all coordinates positive is called the first octant; we shall not refer to any of the other octants by number.

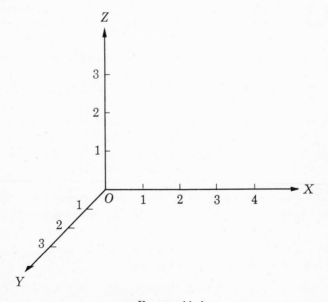

FIGURE 11–1

151

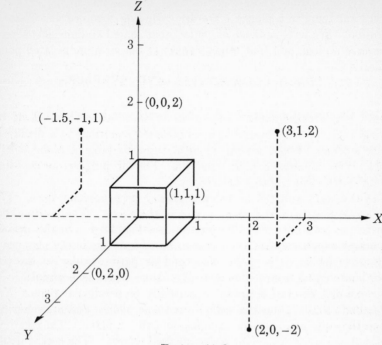

FIGURE 11–2

Having selected a unit of measurement, the position of a point is determined by its distances from the coordinate planes. The distance of a point P from the yz-plane is called the *x-coordinate* of the point. Similarly, the distance from the xz-plane is called the *y-coordinate*, and the distance from the xy-plane the *z-coordinate*. The coordinates of a point are written in the form (x,y,z).

In plotting points and drawing figures, we shall make unit distances on the x- and z-axes equal. A unit distance on the y-axis will be represented by an actual length of about 0.7 of a unit. The y-axis will be drawn at an angle of 135° with the x-axis. This position of the y-axis and the foreshortening in the y-direction aid in visualizing space figures. Notice, for example, the cube and the plotted points in Fig. 11–2.

11–2 The locus of an equation. The locus of an equation in the three-dimensional system is defined exactly as in the case of a two-dimensional system.

The locus of an equation consists of all the points, and only those points, whose coordinates satisfy the given equation.

In the two-dimensional system we found lines and curves as the loci of equations. In three dimensions the locus of an equation is a *surface*.

There are equations whose loci, in three dimensions, are space curves (curves not lying in a plane). We are excluding space curves from consideration. We have noticed, of course, that some two-dimensional equations have no loci, and that others consist of one or more isolated points. Similarly, there are exceptional cases in a three-dimensional system. However, we shall be interested in equations whose loci exist and are surfaces.

11–3 Cylindrical surfaces. We shall begin our study of loci by considering equations in one and two variables. As a further restriction, we shall use equations of only the first and second degrees. The loci of equations of this class are comparatively easy to determine.

To find the locus of the equation

$$x = 4,$$

for example, we notice that the equation is satisfied by giving x the value 4. Since the equation does not contain y or z, no restrictions are placed on these variables. Hence the locus consists of all points which have the x-coordinate equal to 4. The locus is obviously the plane parallel to the yz-plane and 4 units to the right.

Passing now to a linear equation in two variables, we choose for illustration the equation

$$2y + 3z = 6.$$

In the yz-plane this equation represents a line. Consider now a plane through this line and parallel to the x-axis (Fig. 11–3). Any point on this plane has a corresponding point on the line with the same y- and z-coordinates. Hence the coordinates of the point satisfy the given equation. We conclude, therefore, that the plane is the locus of the equation.

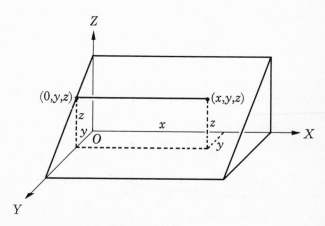

FIGURE 11–3

The two examples indicate the correctness of the following statement:

The locus of a first degree equation in one or two variables is a plane. The plane is parallel to the axis of each missing variable.

Take now the equation

$$(x - 2)^2 + y^2 = 4.$$

In the xy-plane the locus of this equation is a circle of radius 2 and with the center on the x-axis 2 units to the right of the origin (Fig. 11–4). Let $(x,y,0)$ be the coordinates of any point of the circle. Then the point (x,y,z), where z is any real number, satisfies the equation. Thus we see that the locus of the given equation is a surface generated by a line which moves so that it stays parallel to the z-axis and intersects the circle.

A surface generated by a line which moves so that it stays parallel to a fixed line and intersects a fixed curve in a plane is called a *cylindrical surface* or *cylinder*. The curve is called the directrix, and the generating line in any position is called an *element* of the cylinder.

In accordance with this definition, a plane is a special case of a cylinder; the directrix may be a straight line. Hence the locus of each of the three equations which we have considered is a cylinder.

It is easy to generalize the preceding discussion to apply to equations in two variables, even without restriction to the degree, and establish the following theorem.

THEOREM. *The locus of an equation in two variables is a cylinder whose elements are parallel to the axis of the missing variable.*

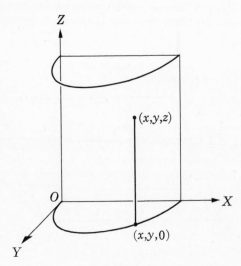

FIGURE 11–4

EXERCISE 11–1

1. Draw the coordinate axes and plot the points: $A(0,0,2)$, $B(0,2,0)$, $C(2,0,0)$, $D(2,3,0)$, $E(3,2,4)$, $F(-2,0,4)$, $G(-1,-1,-1)$, $H(2,1,-2)$.

2. Draw a cube which has the origin and the point $(4,4,4)$ as opposite corners. Write the coordinates of the other corners.

3. Draw the edges of a box which has four of its vertices located at the points $(0,0,0)$, $(3,0,0)$, $(0,2,0)$, and $(0,0,2)$. Write the coordinates of the other vertices.

4. Draw the rectangular parallelepiped which has three of its faces in the coordinate planes and the points $(0,0,0)$ and $(4,5,3)$ as the ends of a diagonal. Write the coordinates of the vertices.

Describe the surface corresponding to each equation 5–24 and make a sketch of the surface.

5. $x = 0$.	6. $y = 0$.	7. $z = 0$.
8. $z = 5$.	9. $z = -5$.	10. $x + y = 4$.
11. $3x + 4z = 12$.	12. $2y + z = 6$.	13. $x + z = 0$.
14. $2x - y = 0$.	15. $3y - z = 6$.	16. $z - 4x = 8$.
17. $x^2 + y^2 = 4$.	18. $(y - 2)^2 + z^2 = 1$.	19. $x^2 = 9z$.
20. $y^2 = 4z$.	21. $(x - 2)^2 = 8y$.	22. $4x^2 + 9y^2 = 36$.
23. $x^2 + z^2 - 4x - 6y + 9 = 0$.	24. $x^2 + 4y^2 - 4x - 32y = 64$.	

11–4 The general linear equation. In rectangular coordinates of two dimensions we found that a linear equation, in either one or two variables, represents a line. In our three-dimensional system we might, by analogy, surmise that linear equations, in one, two, or three variables, represent surfaces of the same type. The surmise is correct. At this point, however, we merely state the fact as a theorem, and reserve the proof for the next chapter.

THEOREM. *The locus, in three dimensions, of the equation*

$$Ax + By + Cz + D = 0,$$

where A, B, and C are not all zero, is a plane.

The location of a plane represented by a linear equation can be determined by finding the lines in which the plane intersects the coordinate planes. These intersections, as well as the intersections which any surface makes with the coordinate planes, are called *traces*.

Consider the equation

$$4x + 3y + 6z = 12.$$

The trace of the locus on the xz-plane has the y-coordinate equal to zero. Hence we set $y = 0$ in the given equation and have

$$4x + 6z = 12$$

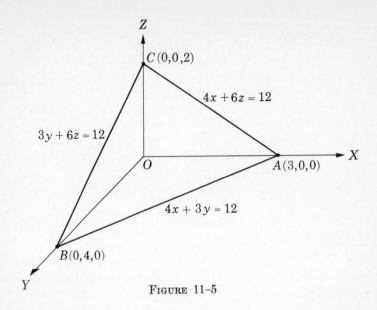

FIGURE 11–5

as the equation of the trace on the xz-plane. The equations of the traces on the xy- and yz-planes are

$$4x + 3y = 12 \quad \text{and} \quad 3y + 6z = 12.$$

Figure 11–5 shows segments of the traces. These segments form a triangle which may be used to picture the plane.

11–5 Second degree equations. The locus of a second degree equation is called a *quadric surface*. In general it is not easy to determine the characteristics and location of a quadric surface corresponding to an equation. We shall use equations of simple type, however, whose loci are more easily studied.

The main device in examining the locus of an equation consists in observing the intersections of the surface by the coordinate planes and planes parallel to them. The idea of symmetry, as in a two-dimensional system, can be used to advantage. If x can be replaced by $-x$ without changing the equation, there is symmetry with respect to the yz-plane. Similar statements apply for the other variables and coordinate planes.

To illustrate the method, we examine the equation

$$x^2 + y^2 = 4z.$$

The surface is symmetric with respect to the yz- and xz-planes. Negative values must not be assigned to z. This tells us that no part of the surface is below the xy-plane. When $z = 0$, $x = 0$ and $y = 0$. Sections made by planes parallel to the xy-plane are circles. This is evident if we substitute

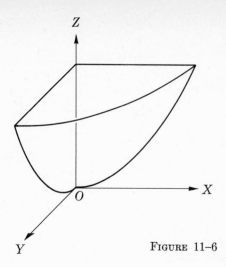

FIGURE 11–6

a positive value for z. The plane $z = 1$, for example, cuts the surface in the circle

$$x^2 + y^2 = 4.$$

Circles of greater radii are obtained as the intersecting plane is taken farther and farther from the xy-plane.

We next substitute $y = 0$ and get the equation

$$x^2 = 4z.$$

Hence the trace in the xz-plane is a parabola. Similarly, the trace in the yz-plane is $y^2 = 4z$.

We now have sufficient information to form a mental picture of the surface. As a matter of interest, though, we observe that sections parallel to the xz- and yz-planes are parabolas. Taking $x = 4$, for example, the equation reduces to

$$y^2 = 4(z - 4).$$

The coordinates of the vertex of this parabola are (4,0,4). Figure 11–6 shows a sketch of the surface in the first octant.

11–6 Quadric surfaces. We shall now discuss a number of second degree, or quadratic, equations which are said to be in standard forms. The study of these equations and their loci, though presently of only geometric interest, furnish information and experience which will prove helpful in other mathematical situations, particularly in the calculus.

A. The ellipsoid. The locus of the equation

$$\frac{x^2}{a^2} + \frac{y^2}{b^2} + \frac{z^2}{c^2} = 1$$

ELLIPSOID

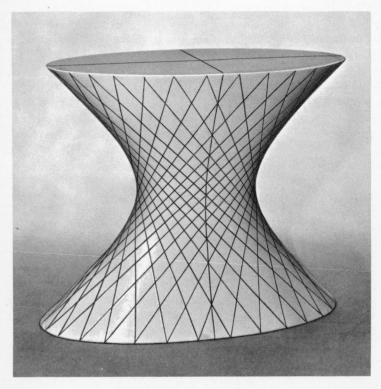

HYPERBOLOID OF ONE SHEET

is called an *ellipsoid*. We see at once that the surface is symmetric with respect to each coordinate plane. By setting one of the variables at a time equal to zero, we find the trace equations to be

$$\frac{x^2}{a^2}+\frac{y^2}{b^2}=1, \quad \frac{x^2}{a^2}+\frac{z^2}{c^2}=1, \quad \frac{y^2}{b^2}+\frac{z^2}{c^2}=1.$$

The traces are all ellipses. Next we assign to x a definite nonzero value, $x=x_0$, and write the given equation as

$$\frac{y^2}{b^2}+\frac{z^2}{c^2}=1-\frac{x_0{}^2}{a^2}.$$

This equation shows that sections made by planes parallel to the yz-plane are ellipses. Further, the elliptic sections decrease in size as the intersecting plane moves farther from the yz-plane. When the moving plane reaches a distance a from the yz-plane, the equation of the section becomes

$$\frac{y^2}{b^2}+\frac{z^2}{c^2}=0,$$

and the intersection, therefore, is a point. No part of the ellipsoid is to the right of the plane $x=a$ or to the left of the plane $x=-a$.

A similar discussion could be made with respect to sections parallel to each of the other coordinate planes. Elliptic sections are obtained for values of z between $-c$ and c, and for values of y between $-b$ and b.

By the method of sections we obtain a clear mental picture of the ellipsoid and a guide for making a sketch (Fig. 11–7).

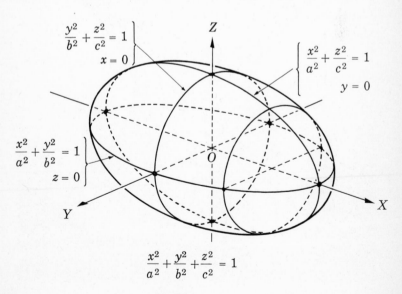

FIGURE 11–7

If two of the three quantities a, b, and c are equal, the sections parallel to one of the coordinate planes are circles. Taking $a = b$ and choosing a permissible value z_0 for z, we have the equation

$$x^2 + y^2 = a^2\left(1 - \frac{z_0^2}{c^2}\right).$$

Thus we see that planes parallel to the xy-plane cut the surface in circles. The ellipsoid for this case could be generated by revolving the xz- or the yz-trace about the z-axis. A surface generated by revolving a curve about a straight line is a *surface of revolution*. Finally, if $a = b = c$, the ellipsoid is a sphere.

B. The hyperboloid of one sheet. The surface represented by the equation

$$\frac{x^2}{a^2} + \frac{y^2}{b^2} - \frac{z^2}{c^2} = 1$$

is called a *hyperboloid of one sheet*. Setting $z = 0$, we get

$$\frac{x^2}{a^2} + \frac{y^2}{b^2} = 1.$$

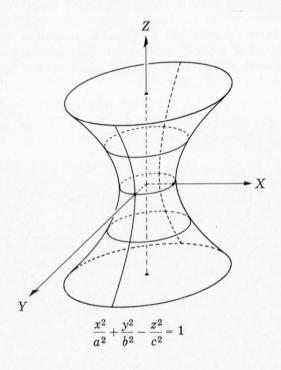

$$\frac{x^2}{a^2} + \frac{y^2}{b^2} - \frac{z^2}{c^2} = 1$$

FIGURE 11–8

Hence the xy-trace is an ellipse. If we replace z in the given equation by a fixed value z_0, we obtain the equation

$$\frac{x^2}{a^2} + \frac{y^2}{b^2} = 1 + \frac{z_0^2}{c^2}.$$

This equation shows that sections parallel to the xy-plane are ellipses and that the sections increase in size as the intersecting plane $z = z_0$ recedes from the origin. If $a = b$, the sections are circles, and the surface is a surface of revolution.

The traces in the xz- and yz-planes are respectively the hyperbolas

$$\frac{x^2}{a^2} - \frac{z^2}{c^2} = 1 \qquad \text{and} \qquad \frac{y^2}{b^2} - \frac{z^2}{c^2} = 1.$$

The sections parallel to the xz- and yz-planes are likewise hyperbolas.

Each of the equations

$$\frac{x^2}{a^2} - \frac{y^2}{b^2} + \frac{z^2}{c^2} = 1 \qquad \text{and} \qquad -\frac{x^2}{a^2} + \frac{y^2}{b^2} + \frac{z^2}{c^2} = 1$$

represents a hyperboloid of one sheet. The first encloses the y-axis and the second the x-axis.

C. The hyperboloid of two sheets. The surface represented by

$$\frac{x^2}{a^2} - \frac{y^2}{b^2} - \frac{z^2}{c^2} = 1$$

is called a *hyperboloid of two sheets.* By setting each variable in turn equal to zero, we get the equations

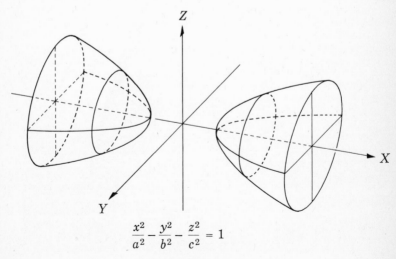

$$\frac{x^2}{a^2} - \frac{y^2}{b^2} - \frac{z^2}{c^2} = 1$$

FIGURE 11–9

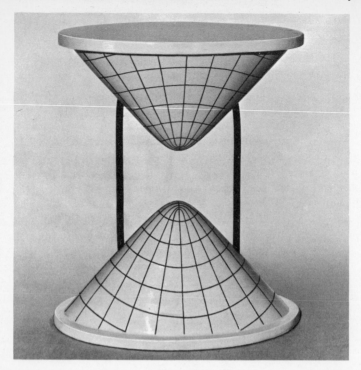

HYPERBOLOID OF TWO SHEETS

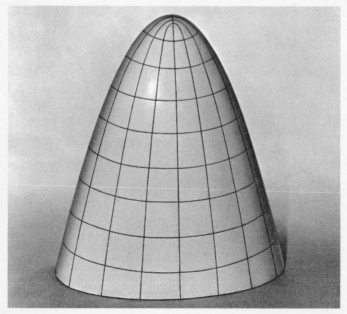

ELLIPTIC PARABOLOID

$$\frac{x^2}{a^2} - \frac{y^2}{b^2} = 1, \quad \frac{x^2}{a^2} - \frac{z^2}{c^2} = 1, \quad -\frac{y^2}{b^2} - \frac{z^2}{c^2} = 1.$$

The first two equations show that the xy- and xz-traces are hyperbolas. The third tells us there is no trace in the yz-plane. The sections made by the plane $x = x_0$ is given by the equation

$$\frac{y^2}{b^2} + \frac{z^2}{c^2} = \frac{x_0^2}{a^2} - 1.$$

This equation represents a point or an ellipse according as the numerical value of x_0 is equal to or greater than a. Sections parallel to the xz- and xy-planes are hyperbolas. From this information the surface (Fig. 11–9) is readily visualized.

If $b = c$, the hyperboloid of two sheets is a surface of revolution.

Hyperboloids of two sheets are also represented by the equations

$$-\frac{x^2}{a^2} - \frac{y^2}{b^2} + \frac{z^2}{c^2} = 1 \quad \text{and} \quad -\frac{x^2}{a^2} + \frac{y^2}{b^2} - \frac{z^2}{c^2} = 1.$$

D. *The elliptic paraboloid.* The locus of the equation

$$\frac{x^2}{a^2} + \frac{y^2}{b^2} = c^2 z$$

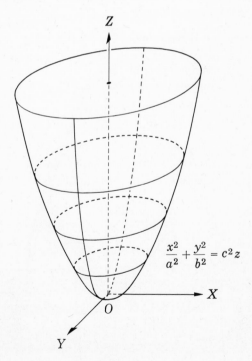

$$\frac{x^2}{a^2} + \frac{y^2}{b^2} = c^2 z$$

FIGURE 11–10

is called an *elliptic paraboloid*. The xy-trace, obtained by setting $z = 0$, is the origin. No part of the surface lies below the xy-plane because there are no real values for x and y corresponding to a negative z. Planes parallel to and above the xy-plane make elliptic sections which increase in size as the plane recedes from the origin.

The traces in the xz- and yz-planes are respectively the parabolas

$$\frac{x^2}{a^2} = c^2 z \quad \text{and} \quad \frac{y^2}{b^2} = c^2 z.$$

The surface is sketched in Fig. 11-10.

If $a = b$, the sections parallel to the xy-plane are circles. For this case the surface is obtainable by rotating either the xz- or yz-trace about the z-axis.

Elliptic paraboloids are also represented by the equations

$$\frac{x^2}{a^2} + \frac{z^2}{c^2} = b^2 y \quad \text{and} \quad \frac{y^2}{b^2} + \frac{z^2}{c^2} = a^2 x.$$

E. The hyperbolic paraboloid. The locus of the equation

$$\frac{x^2}{a^2} - \frac{y^2}{b^2} = c^2 z$$

is called a *hyperbolic paraboloid*. The xy-trace is given by the equation

$$\frac{x^2}{a^2} - \frac{y^2}{b^2} = 0 \quad \text{or} \quad \left(\frac{x}{a} + \frac{y}{b}\right)\left(\frac{x}{a} - \frac{y}{b}\right) = 0.$$

This equation represents a pair of lines intersecting at the origin. The sections made by the plane $z = z_0$ is the hyperbola

$$\frac{x^2}{a^2} - \frac{y^2}{b^2} = c^2 z_0.$$

The hyperbola has its transverse axis parallel to the x-axis when z_0 is positive and parallel to the y-axis when z_0 is negative.

Sections by planes parallel to the xz-plane and the yz-plane are parabolas.

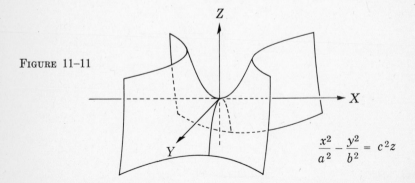

FIGURE 11-11

$$\frac{x^2}{a^2} - \frac{y^2}{b^2} = c^2 z$$

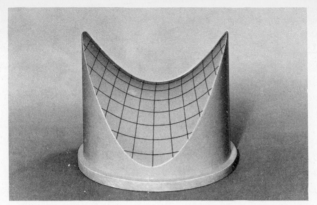

HYPERBOLIC PARABOLOID

Further aid in visualizing the surface may be had from Fig. 11–11. A hyperbolic paraboloid is also represented by each of the equations

$$\frac{x^2}{a^2} - \frac{z^2}{c^2} = b^2 y \qquad \text{and} \qquad \frac{y^2}{b^2} - \frac{z^2}{c^2} = a^2 x.$$

F. The elliptic cone. The locus of the equation

$$\frac{x^2}{a^2} + \frac{y^2}{b^2} = \frac{z^2}{c^2}$$

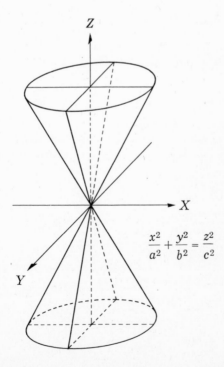

$$\frac{x^2}{a^2} + \frac{y^2}{b^2} = \frac{z^2}{c^2}$$

FIGURE 11–12

is an *elliptic cone*.   Setting x, y, and z in turn equal to zero, we have the trace equations

$$\frac{x^2}{a^2} + \frac{y^2}{b^2} = 0, \quad \frac{x^2}{a^2} = \frac{z^2}{c^2}, \quad \frac{y^2}{b^2} = \frac{z^2}{c^2}.$$

These equations reveal that the xy-trace is the origin, and that each of the other traces is a pair of lines intersecting at the origin.

Sections parallel to the xy-plane are ellipses, and those parallel to the other coordinate planes are hyperbolas.

For the case in which $a = b$, the cone is a right circular cone.

Elliptic cones are also represented by the equations

$$\frac{x^2}{a^2} + \frac{z^2}{c^2} = \frac{y^2}{b^2} \quad \text{and} \quad \frac{y^2}{b^2} + \frac{z^2}{c^2} = \frac{x^2}{a^2}.$$

Exercise 11–2

Draw the traces on the coordinate planes:

1. $2x + 3y + 4z = 12$.
2. $2x + y + 2z = 4$.
3. $x - 4y + z = 4$.
4. $2x + 3y - z = 6$.
5. $x + y - z = 0$.
6. $x - y - z = 0$.

Identify and sketch each quadric surface. If preferred, make the sketch in the first octant only and state the symmetry with respect to the coordinate planes:

7. $\dfrac{x^2}{9} + \dfrac{y^2}{4} + \dfrac{z^2}{16} = 1$.
8. $\dfrac{x^2}{9} + \dfrac{y^2}{9} + \dfrac{z^2}{4} = 1$.

9. $x^2 + y^2 + z^2 = 16$.
10. $x^2 + y^2 + 4z^2 = 4$.

11. $\dfrac{x^2}{9} + \dfrac{y^2}{16} - \dfrac{z^2}{4} = 1$.
12. $\dfrac{x^2}{4} - \dfrac{y^2}{4} + \dfrac{z^2}{9} = 1$.

13. $x^2 + y^2 - z^2 = 16$.
14. $x^2 - y^2 - z^2 = 16$.

15. $\dfrac{x^2}{16} - \dfrac{y^2}{9} - \dfrac{z^2}{4} = 1$.
16. $\dfrac{y^2}{4} - \dfrac{z^2}{9} - \dfrac{x^2}{9} = 1$.

17. $\dfrac{x^2}{9} + \dfrac{y^2}{4} = 2z$.
18. $\dfrac{x^2}{4} + \dfrac{z^2}{1} = 3y$.

19. $y^2 + z^2 = 4x$.
20. $x^2 - y^2 = 4z$.

21. $\dfrac{x^2}{9} - \dfrac{y^2}{16} = \dfrac{z}{4}$.
22. $\dfrac{x^2}{4} - \dfrac{z^2}{4} = 2y$.

23. $\dfrac{x^2}{16} + \dfrac{y^2}{9} = \dfrac{z^2}{4}$.
24. $\dfrac{y^2}{4} + \dfrac{z^2}{4} = x^2$.

CHAPTER 12

VECTORS AND PLANES AND LINES

12–1 Vectors.   There are two special kinds of physical quantities which are dealt with extensively in physics and in mathematics.   One kind has magnitude only, and the other has magnitude and direction.   A quantity which has magnitude only is called a *scalar*.   The length of an object, expressed in terms of a chosen unit of length, is a scalar.   Mass, time, and density are other illustrations of scalars.   A quantity which has both magnitude and direction is called a *vector*.   Forces, velocities, and accelerations are examples of vectors.   These quantities have direction as well as magnitude.

A vector is customarily represented by an arrow.   The length of the arrow represents the magnitude of the vector and the arrow is pointed in the assigned direction.   Thus a force, for example, could be represented graphically by an arrow pointing in the direction in which the force acts and having a length (in a convenient unit) equal to the magnitude of the force.

Two vectors are said to be *equal* if they are parallel, have the same magnitude (length), and point the same way.   The vectors **A** and **B** in Fig. 12–1 are equal.   If a vector has the same magnitude as **A** and points in the opposite direction, it is denoted by −**A**.*

As might be inferred from the definition, vectors are of great importance in physics and engineering.   They are also used to much advantage in pure mathematics.   The study of solid analytic geometry, in particular, is facilitated by the application of the vector concept.   Our immediate objective in the introduction of vectors, however, is their use in dealing with planes and lines in space.   To pursue this study, it is necessary first to consider certain operations on vectors.

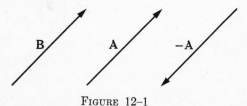

FIGURE 12–1

---

* The **bold-faced** type indicates that the letter represents a vector.

167

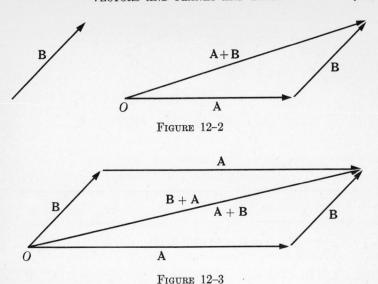

FIGURE 12-2

FIGURE 12-3

12-2 Operations on vectors. It may be observed that a directed line segment (Section 2-1) is a vector. In numerous places we have added and subtracted directed line segments. In all these cases the vectors have had the same, or the opposite, directions. To obtain the sum or the difference of two such vectors, we have applied the usual method of adding and subtracting algebraic quantities. We now define the sum and difference of two vectors where there is no restriction as to their directions.

To find the sum of two vectors **A** and **B**, we draw from the head of **A** a vector equal to **B**. The sum of **A** and **B** is then defined as the vector drawn from the origin of **A** to the head of **B** (Fig. 12-2).

Since the opposite sides of a parallelogram are equal and parallel, it may be seen from Fig. 12-3 that the sum of two vectors is independent of the order in which they are added. That is,

$$\mathbf{A} + \mathbf{B} = \mathbf{B} + \mathbf{A}.$$

Hence vectors are said to be *commutative* with respect to addition.

The sum of three vectors **A**, **B**, and **C** may be obtained by adding **C** to **A** + **B**. It is easy to show geometrically that the sum of three or more vectors is independent of the order of addition. For example,

$$\mathbf{A} + \mathbf{B} + \mathbf{C} = (\mathbf{A} + \mathbf{B}) + \mathbf{C} = \mathbf{A} + (\mathbf{B} + \mathbf{C}).$$

This is called the *associative law* of addition.

To subtract the vector **B** from the vector **A**, we first draw the vectors from a common origin (Fig. 12-4). Then the vector extending from the end of **B** to the end of **A** and pointing toward the end of **A** is defined as the

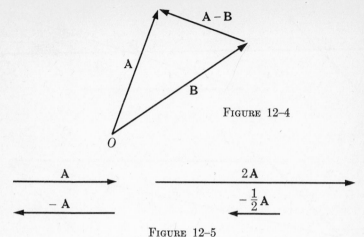

FIGURE 12–4

FIGURE 12–5

difference $\mathbf{A} - \mathbf{B}$.   The triangle formed by the vectors $\mathbf{B}$, $\mathbf{A} - \mathbf{B}$, and $\mathbf{A}$ shows that

$$\mathbf{B} + (\mathbf{A} - \mathbf{B}) = \mathbf{A}.$$

That is, $\mathbf{A} - \mathbf{B}$ is the vector which added to $\mathbf{B}$ gives $\mathbf{A}$.

The product of a scalar m and a vector $\mathbf{A}$, expressed by $m\mathbf{A}$, is a vector m times as long as $\mathbf{A}$, and has the direction of $\mathbf{A}$ if m is positive, and the opposite direction if m is negative.   If $m = 0$, the product is a zero vector. If $m = -1$, the product is $-\mathbf{A}$.   (See Fig. 12–5.)

If m and n are scalars, the sum of $m\mathbf{A}$ and $n\mathbf{A}$ is a vector $m + n$ times as long as $\mathbf{A}$.   This is expressed by

$$m\mathbf{A} + n\mathbf{A} = (m + n)\mathbf{A}. \tag{1}$$

The vectors $\mathbf{A}$ and $\mathbf{B}$ and $\mathbf{A} + \mathbf{B}$ form the sides of a triangle (Fig. 12–2). If each of these vectors is multiplied by a scalar m, then $m\mathbf{A}$, $m\mathbf{B}$, and $m(\mathbf{A} + \mathbf{B})$ form a similar triangle, and hence

$$m(\mathbf{A} + \mathbf{B}) = m\mathbf{A} + m\mathbf{B}. \tag{2}$$

Equations (1) and (2) show that vectors and scalars obey the *distributive law* of multiplication.

12–3 Vectors in a rectangular coordinate plane.   Vectors are conveniently dealt with when they are expressed as the sum of vectors parallel to the coordinate axes.   The letters $\mathbf{i}$ and $\mathbf{j}$ are usually employed to represent vectors of unit length from the origin to the points $(1,0)$ and $(0,1)$ respectively.   Any vector in the plane can be expressed as the sum of a scalar times $\mathbf{i}$ and a scalar times $\mathbf{j}$.   Thus the vector $\mathbf{V}$ (Fig. 12–6) may be written as

$$\mathbf{V} = a\mathbf{i} + b\mathbf{j}.$$

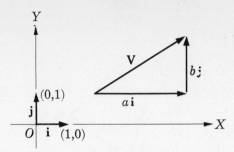

FIGURE 12–6

The vectors $a\mathbf{i}$ and $b\mathbf{j}$ are called the *components* of $\mathbf{V}$. The vector $a\mathbf{i}$ is the x-component and $b\mathbf{j}$ is the y-component. The lengths of $\mathbf{V}$, $a\mathbf{i}$, and $b\mathbf{j}$ are denoted respectively by the symbols $|\mathbf{V}|$, $|a|$, and $|b|$. These quantities, by the Pythagorean theorem, satisfy the relation

$$|\mathbf{V}| = \sqrt{a^2 + b^2}.$$

The quotient of $\mathbf{V}$ and $|\mathbf{V}|$ is a vector of unit length in the direction of $\mathbf{V}$. A vector is called a *unit vector* if its length is unity.

If $\mathbf{V}_1$ and $\mathbf{V}_2$ are vectors in terms of their components

$$\mathbf{V}_1 = a_1\mathbf{i} + b_1\mathbf{j}, \quad \mathbf{V}_2 = a_2\mathbf{i} + b_2\mathbf{j},$$

then

$$\mathbf{V}_1 + \mathbf{V}_2 = (a_1 + a_2)\mathbf{i} + (b_1 + b_2)\mathbf{j}.$$

Thus the sum is a vector whose x- and y-components are the sums of the x- and y-components respectively of the two given vectors.

Similarly, we have

$$\mathbf{V}_1 - \mathbf{V}_2 = (a_1 - a_2)\mathbf{i} + (b_1 - b_2)\mathbf{j}.$$

EXAMPLE 1. Vectors are drawn from the origin to the points $A(3,-2)$ and $B(1,5)$. Indicating these vectors by $\overrightarrow{OA} = \mathbf{A}$ and $\overrightarrow{OB} = \mathbf{B}$, find $\mathbf{A} + \mathbf{B}$ and $\mathbf{A} - \mathbf{B}$.

Solution. The vectors (Fig. 12–7) are

$$\mathbf{A} = 3\mathbf{i} - 2\mathbf{j}, \quad \mathbf{B} = \mathbf{i} + 5\mathbf{j}.$$

Their sum is

$$\mathbf{A} + \mathbf{B} = 4\mathbf{i} + 3\mathbf{j},$$

and their difference is

$$\mathbf{A} - \mathbf{B} = 2\mathbf{i} - 7\mathbf{j}.$$

EXAMPLE 2. Find the vector from the origin to the point $\frac{2}{3}$ of the way from $A(1,3)$ to $B(4,-3)$.

Solution. The required vector is equal to the vector from the origin to A plus $\frac{2}{3}$ of the vector from the point A to the point B. Indicating the vectors from the origin to A and B by $\mathbf{A}$ and $\mathbf{B}$ respectively, we have

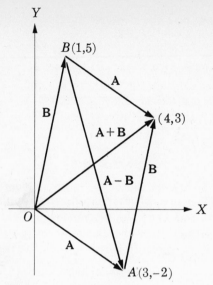

FIGURE 12–7

$$\mathbf{A} = \mathbf{i} + 3\mathbf{j},$$
$$\mathbf{B} = 4\mathbf{i} - 3\mathbf{j},$$
$$\mathbf{B} - \mathbf{A} = 3\mathbf{i} - 6\mathbf{j}.$$

Hence the required vector $\mathbf{V}$ is

$$\mathbf{V} = \mathbf{i} + 3\mathbf{j} + \tfrac{2}{3}(3\mathbf{i} - 6\mathbf{j})$$
$$= 3\mathbf{i} - \mathbf{j}.$$

EXERCISE 12–1

In problems 1–4 find the sum of the vectors from the origin to the given points. Also subtract the second vector from the first. Draw all vectors.

1. $A(2,3)$, $B(-4,5)$. 2. $A(5,0)$, $B(0,4)$.
3. $A(3,-2)$, $B(-1,-4)$. 4. $A(6,7)$, $B(-5,-5)$.

Determine a unit vector having the direction of the vector in each problem 5–8.

5. $3\mathbf{i} + 4\mathbf{j}$. 6. $3\mathbf{i} - 12\mathbf{j}$. 7. $12\mathbf{i} - 5\mathbf{j}$.
8. $2\mathbf{i} - 3\mathbf{j}$. 9. $\mathbf{i} + 2\mathbf{j}$. 10. $4\mathbf{i} + 3\mathbf{j}$.

Find the length of each vector 9–12 and the cosine of the angle which the vector makes with the positive x-axis.

11. $\mathbf{i} + \mathbf{j}$. 12. $-\mathbf{i} + 3\mathbf{j}$. 13. $\mathbf{i} + 0\mathbf{j}$.
14. $0\mathbf{i} + 3\mathbf{j}$. 15. $-3\mathbf{i} + 2\mathbf{j}$. 16. $5\mathbf{i} + 12\mathbf{j}$.

17. Find the vector from the origin to the mid-point of the vector $\overrightarrow{P_1 P_2}$ joining $P_1(3,6)$ and $P_2(5,-8)$.

18. Find the vectors from the origin to the trisection points of the vector $\overrightarrow{P_1P_2}$ joining the points $P_1(-3,4)$ and $P_2(12,-5)$.

12–4 Vectors in space. In the three-dimensional rectangular coordinate system the unit vectors from the origin to the points $(1,0,0)$, $(0,1,0)$, and $(0,0,1)$ are denoted respectively by $\mathbf{i}$, $\mathbf{j}$, and $\mathbf{k}$. Any vector in space can be expressed in terms of these unit vectors. Thus the vector from the origin to the point $A(a,b,c)$ is

$$\overrightarrow{OA} = \mathbf{A} = a\mathbf{i} + b\mathbf{j} + c\mathbf{k}.$$

The vectors $a\mathbf{i}$, $b\mathbf{j}$, and $c\mathbf{k}$ are the x-, y-, and z-components of the vector $\mathbf{A}$. The length of the vector $\mathbf{A}$ may be obtained by using the lengths of the sides of the right triangles OCA and ODC (Fig. 12–8). From the Pythagorean relation, we have

$$\begin{aligned}
(OA)^2 &= (OC)^2 + (CA)^2 \\
&= (OD)^2 + (DC)^2 + (CA)^2 \\
&= a^2 + b^2 + c^2.
\end{aligned}$$

Hence the length of $\mathbf{A}$ is

$$|\mathbf{A}| = \sqrt{a^2 + b^2 + c^2}.$$

The vector from $P_1(x_1,y_1,z_1)$ to $P_2(x_2,y_2,z_2)$ in Fig. 12–9 has the components $(x_2 - x_1)\mathbf{i}$, $(y_2 - y_1)\mathbf{j}$, $(z_2 - z_1)\mathbf{k}$. Hence it is expressed by

$$\overrightarrow{P_1P_2} = (x_2 - x_1)\mathbf{i} + (y_2 - y_1)\mathbf{j} + (z_2 - z_1)\mathbf{k}.$$

The length of the vector $\overrightarrow{P_1P_2}$, or the distance d between the points P_1 and P_2, is

$$d = \sqrt{(x_2 - x_1)^2 + (y_2 - y_1)^2 + (z_2 - z_1)^2}.$$

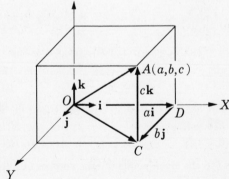

FIGURE 12–8

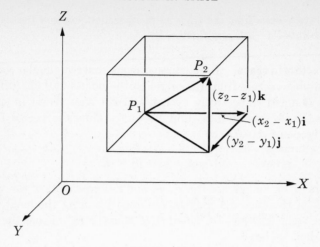

Figure 12–9

EXAMPLE. The points $A(1,-2,3)$, $B(-4,5,6)$, and $C(5,7,0)$ are vertices of a triangle. Express the sides as vectors and find the length of each side.

Solution. The vectors from the origin to the given points are

$$\vec{OA} = \mathbf{A} = \mathbf{i} - 2\mathbf{j} + 3\mathbf{k},$$
$$\vec{OB} = \mathbf{B} = -4\mathbf{i} + 5\mathbf{j} + 6\mathbf{k},$$
$$\vec{OC} = \mathbf{C} = 5\mathbf{i} + 7\mathbf{j}.$$

The sides, expressed as vectors, are

$$\vec{AB} = \mathbf{B} - \mathbf{A} = -5\mathbf{i} + 7\mathbf{j} + 3\mathbf{k},$$
$$\vec{BC} = \mathbf{C} - \mathbf{B} = 9\mathbf{i} + 2\mathbf{j} - 6\mathbf{k},$$
$$\vec{CA} = \mathbf{A} - \mathbf{C} = -4\mathbf{i} - 9\mathbf{j} + 3\mathbf{k}.$$

The lengths of the vectors are

$$|\vec{AB}| = \sqrt{(-5)^2 + 7^2 + 3^2} = \sqrt{83},$$
$$|\vec{BC}| = \sqrt{9^2 + 2^2 + (-6)^2} = 11,$$
$$|\vec{CA}| = \sqrt{(-4)^2 + (-9)^2 + 3^2} = \sqrt{106}.$$

EXERCISE 12–2

Find the distance between the points A and B in each problem 1–4.

1. $A(-3,2,0)$, $B(6,-4,2)$.   2. $A(3,1,4)$, $B(1,-1,-2)$.
3. $A(5,7,1)$, $B(6,-3,2)$.   4. $A(4,4,0)$, $B(-2,1,-2)$.

In each problem 5–8 the given points are the vertices of a triangle. Determine the vectors $\vec{AB}$, $\vec{BC}$, and $\vec{CA}$ and the lengths of these vectors.

5. $A(6,8,1)$, $B(0,2,1)$, $C(0,-4,-5)$.

6. $A(2,3,-2)$, $B(-2,1,3)$, $C(3,8,0)$.

7. $A(3,3,3)$, $B(4,5,5)$, $C(1,2,5)$.

8. $A(2,4,5)$, $B(6,8,-1)$, $C(-2,-2,1)$.

Determine a unit vector having the direction of the vector in each problem 9–12.

9. $6i + 3j - 6k$.　　　　　　　10. $2i - 4j + 4k$.

11. $2i - j - 3k$.　　　　　　　12. $i + j + k$.

13. Find the vectors from the origin to the mid-point and the trisection points of the line segment $(1,-3,7)$, $(7,3,-2)$. What are the coordinates of the terminal points of these vectors?

14. Find the equation of a sphere of radius 5 and center at $(1,-2,3)$.

15. Find the center and radius of the sphere $x^2 + y^2 + z^2 + 4x - 2y + 6z = 0$.

16. Find the coordinates of the points which divide the line segment $(4,5,7)$, $(2,3,5)$ into four equal parts.

17. Find the vector from the origin to the intersection of the medians of the triangle whose vertices are $A(4,2,1)$, $B(-5,7,0)$, and $C(4,-3,5)$.

18. The line segment $(3,4,6)$, $(-1,1,0)$ is produced by its own length through each end. Find the coordinates of the new ends.

12–5 The scalar product of two vectors. So far we have not defined a product of two vectors. Actually there are two kinds of products of two vectors which have arisen in physics and are extensively used. We shall define one of these products and make some applications to geometry.

The *scalar product* of two vectors **A** and **B**, denoted by **A** · **B**, is defined by the equation

$$\mathbf{A} \cdot \mathbf{B} = |\mathbf{A}|\,|\mathbf{B}| \cos\theta,$$

where θ is the angle between the vectors when drawn from a common origin (Fig. 12–10). It makes no difference whether θ is taken as positive or negative, since $\cos\theta = \cos(-\theta)$. However, we shall restrict θ to the range from $0°$ to $180°$. The angle θ is $0°$ if **A** and **B** point in the same direction, and is equal to $180°$ if they point oppositely. The name *scalar* is used because the product is a scalar quantity. This product is also called the *dot product*, since the product is indicated by placing a dot between the two vectors.

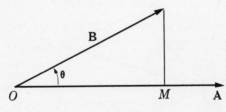

FIGURE 12–10

In the figure the point M is the foot of the perpendicular to the vector **A** drawn from the point of **B**. The vector from O to M is called the *vector projection* of **B** on **A**. The vector projection and **A** point in the same direction, since θ is an acute angle. If θ exceeds 90°, then **A** and the vector from O to M point oppositely. The *scalar projection* of **B** on **A** is defined as $|\mathbf{B}| \cos \theta$. The sign of the scalar projection depends on $\cos \theta$. Using the idea of scalar projection of one vector on another, the dot product may be interpreted geometrically as

$$\mathbf{A} \cdot \mathbf{B} = |\mathbf{A}|\,|\mathbf{B}| \cos \theta$$

$$= \text{(length of } \mathbf{A}) \text{ times (the scalar projection of } \mathbf{B} \text{ on } \mathbf{A}).$$

We could also say that the dot product of **A** and **B** is the length of **B** times the scalar projection of **A** on **B**.

It follows immediately from the definition of scalar product that

$$\mathbf{A} \cdot \mathbf{B} = \mathbf{B} \cdot \mathbf{A}. \tag{1}$$

Hence the dot product of two vectors is said to be *commutative*.

We next establish the *distributive* law from the scalar multiplication of vectors. If we let b and c stand for the scalar projections of **B** and **C** on **A**, we see (Fig. 12–11) that the sum of the scalar projections of **B** and **C** on **A** is the same as the scalar projection of $(\mathbf{B} + \mathbf{C})$ on **A**. Hence

$$|\mathbf{A}|(b + c) = |\mathbf{A}|b + |\mathbf{A}|c,$$

and

$$\mathbf{A} \cdot (\mathbf{B} + \mathbf{C}) = \mathbf{A} \cdot \mathbf{B} + \mathbf{A} \cdot \mathbf{C}. \tag{2}$$

Equation (2) expresses the distributive law for the multiplication of vectors. Since the dot product is commutative [equation (1)], we have also

$$(\mathbf{B} + \mathbf{C}) \cdot \mathbf{A} = \mathbf{B} \cdot \mathbf{A} + \mathbf{C} \cdot \mathbf{A}. \tag{3}$$

From equations (2) and (3) it may be seen that the scalar product of two sums of vectors may be carried out as in multiplying two algebraic expressions, each of which consists of more than one term. Thus, for example,

$$(\mathbf{A} + \mathbf{B}) \cdot (\mathbf{C} + \mathbf{D}) = \mathbf{A} \cdot \mathbf{C} + \mathbf{A} \cdot \mathbf{D} + \mathbf{B} \cdot \mathbf{C} + \mathbf{B} \cdot \mathbf{D}.$$

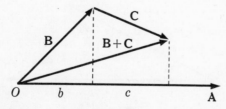

FIGURE 12–11

If two vectors are expressed in terms of $\mathbf{i}$, $\mathbf{j}$, and $\mathbf{k}$, the scalar product can be found in a simple way.   Let the vectors $\mathbf{A}$ and $\mathbf{B}$ be expressed as

$$\mathbf{A} = a_1\mathbf{i} + a_2\mathbf{j} + a_3\mathbf{k},$$
$$\mathbf{B} = b_1\mathbf{i} + b_2\mathbf{j} + b_3\mathbf{k}.$$

To obtain the dot product of $\mathbf{A}$ and $\mathbf{B}$, we first determine the dot products of the unit vectors $\mathbf{i}$, $\mathbf{j}$, and $\mathbf{k}$.   We have

$$\mathbf{i} \cdot \mathbf{i} = \mathbf{j} \cdot \mathbf{j} = \mathbf{k} \cdot \mathbf{k} = 1,$$
$$\mathbf{i} \cdot \mathbf{j} = \mathbf{j} \cdot \mathbf{k} = \mathbf{k} \cdot \mathbf{i} = 0.$$

Hence we obtain

$$\mathbf{A} \cdot \mathbf{B} = a_1b_1 + a_2b_2 + a_3b_3. \tag{4}$$

Equation (4) shows that the dot product is obtained by the simple process of adding the products of the corresponding coefficients of $\mathbf{i}$, $\mathbf{j}$, and $\mathbf{k}$.

Since $\cos 90° = 0$ and $\cos 0° = 1$, it is evident that the scalar product of two perpendicular vectors is zero, and the scalar product of two vectors in the same direction is the product of their lengths.   The dot product of a vector on itself is the square of the length of the vector.   That is,

$$\mathbf{A} \cdot \mathbf{A} = |\mathbf{A}|^2.$$

EXAMPLE 1. Determine whether the vectors

$$\mathbf{A} = 3\mathbf{i} + 4\mathbf{j} - 8\mathbf{k},$$
$$\mathbf{B} = 4\mathbf{i} - 7\mathbf{j} - 2\mathbf{k}$$

are perpendicular.

Solution.   The scalar product is

$$\mathbf{A} \cdot \mathbf{B} = 12 - 28 + 16 = 0.$$

Since this product is zero, the vectors are perpendicular.

EXAMPLE 2. Vectors are drawn from the origin to the points $A(6,-3,2)$ and $B(-2,1,2)$.   Find the angle AOB.

Solution.   Indicating $\overrightarrow{OA}$ by $\mathbf{A}$ and $\overrightarrow{OB}$ by $\mathbf{B}$, we write

$$\mathbf{A} = 6\mathbf{i} - 3\mathbf{j} + 2\mathbf{k},$$
$$\mathbf{B} = -2\mathbf{i} + \mathbf{j} + 2\mathbf{k}.$$

To find the angle, we substitute in both members of the equation

$$\mathbf{A} \cdot \mathbf{B} = |\mathbf{A}|\,|\mathbf{B}|\cos\theta.$$

The product in the left member is $\mathbf{A} \cdot \mathbf{B} = -12 - 3 + 4 = -11$.   The lengths of $\mathbf{A}$ and $\mathbf{B}$ are $|\mathbf{A}| = \sqrt{36 + 9 + 4} = 7$, $|\mathbf{B}| = \sqrt{4 + 1 + 4} = 3$.   Hence

$$\cos\theta = \frac{\mathbf{A} \cdot \mathbf{B}}{|\mathbf{A}|\,|\mathbf{B}|} = \frac{-11}{21},$$

$$\theta = \cos^{-1}\frac{-11}{21} = 122° \text{ (nearest degree)}.$$

EXAMPLE 3.   Find the scalar projection and the vector projection of

$$\mathbf{B} = 2\mathbf{i} - 3\mathbf{j} - \mathbf{k} \text{ on } \mathbf{A} = 3\mathbf{i} - 6\mathbf{j} + 2\mathbf{k}.$$

Solution.   The scalar projection of **B** on **A** is $|\mathbf{B}| \cos \theta$, where θ is the angle between the vectors.   Using the equation

$$\mathbf{A} \cdot \mathbf{B} = |\mathbf{A}| \, |\mathbf{B}| \cos \theta,$$

we have

$$|\mathbf{B}| \cos \theta = \frac{\mathbf{A} \cdot \mathbf{B}}{|\mathbf{A}|}.$$

Since $\mathbf{A} \cdot \mathbf{B} = 6 + 18 - 2 = 22$ and $|\mathbf{A}| = \sqrt{9 + 36 + 4} = 7$, it follows that

$$|\mathbf{B}| \cos \theta = \tfrac{22}{7}.$$

The scalar projection of **B** on **A** is $22/7$.   Since the scalar projection is positive, the vector projection is in the direction of **A**.   The vector projection is therefore the product of the scalar projection and a unit vector in the direction of **A**.   This unit vector is **A** divided by its length.   Hence the vector projection of **B** on **A** is

$$\frac{22}{7} \cdot \frac{3\mathbf{i} - 6\mathbf{j} + 2\mathbf{k}}{7} = \frac{22}{49} (3\mathbf{i} - 6\mathbf{j} + 2\mathbf{k}).$$

EXERCISE 12–3

Find the dot product of the vectors in each problem 1–4.   Find also the cosine of the angle between the vectors.

1. $\mathbf{A} = 4\mathbf{i} - \mathbf{j} + 8\mathbf{k}$,
   $\mathbf{B} = 2\mathbf{i} + 2\mathbf{j} - \mathbf{k}$.

2. $\mathbf{A} = 5\mathbf{i} - 3\mathbf{j} + 2\mathbf{k}$,
   $\mathbf{B} = -\mathbf{i} + 7\mathbf{j} + 13\mathbf{k}$.

3. $\mathbf{A} = 10\mathbf{i} + 2\mathbf{j} + 11\mathbf{k}$,
   $\mathbf{B} = 4\mathbf{i} - 8\mathbf{j} - \mathbf{k}$.

4. $\mathbf{A} = \mathbf{i} + \mathbf{j} + 2\mathbf{k}$,
   $\mathbf{B} = 8\mathbf{i} + 4\mathbf{j} + \mathbf{k}$.

In each problem 5 and 6 find the scalar projection and the vector projection of **B** on **A**.

5. $\mathbf{A} = \mathbf{i} - \mathbf{j} - \mathbf{k}$,
   $\mathbf{B} = 10\mathbf{i} - 11\mathbf{j} + 2\mathbf{k}$.

6. $\mathbf{A} = 3\mathbf{i} + 3\mathbf{j} + \mathbf{k}$,
   $\mathbf{B} = \mathbf{i} - 2\mathbf{j} - 2\mathbf{k}$.

7. Find the angle which a diagonal of a cube makes with one of its edges.

8. From a vertex of a cube, a diagonal of a face and a diagonal of the cube are drawn.   Find the angle thus formed.

The points in problems 9 and 10 are vertices of a triangle.   In each determine the vector from A to B and the vector from A to C.   Find the angle between these vectors.   Similarly, find the other interior angles of the triangle.

9. $A(3,4,2)$, $B(1,7,1)$, $C(-2,3,-5)$.

10. $A(-2,-1,1)$, $B(1,0,-2)$, $C(0,-3,1)$.

11. Let α, β, and γ denote the angles which the vector $\mathbf{A} = a\mathbf{i} + b\mathbf{j} + c\mathbf{k}$ makes with the positive x-, y-, and z-axes respectively.   Using $\mathbf{A} \cdot \mathbf{i}$, $\mathbf{A} \cdot \mathbf{j}$, and $\mathbf{A} \cdot \mathbf{k}$, find $\cos \alpha$, $\cos \beta$, and $\cos \gamma$.   The cosines of α, β, and γ are called the *direction cosines* of the vector **A**.   Show that $\cos^2 \alpha + \cos^2 \beta + \cos^2 \gamma = 1$.

12–6 The equation of a plane. We have discovered (Section 11–3) that a linear equation in one or two variables represents a plane. In Section 11–4, we stated without proof that a linear equation in three variables also represents a plane. We shall now prove that the locus of a linear equation, in one, two, or three variables, is a plane.

Suppose that a point $P_1(x_1,y_1,z_1)$ is in a given plane and that a nonzero vector

$$\mathbf{N} = A\mathbf{i} + B\mathbf{j} + C\mathbf{k}$$

is perpendicular, or normal, to the plane (Fig. 12–12). A point $P(x,y,z)$ will lie in the given plane if and only if the vector $\overrightarrow{P_1P}$ is perpendicular to $\mathbf{N}$. Setting the scalar product of these vectors equal to zero, we obtain the equation

$$\mathbf{N} \cdot \overrightarrow{P_1P} = 0, \tag{1}$$

or

$$A(x - x_1) + B(y - y_1) + C(z - z_1) = 0. \tag{2}$$

This is the equation of the plane which passes through $P_1(x_1,y_1,z_1)$ and is perpendicular to the vector $\mathbf{N} = A\mathbf{i} + B\mathbf{j} + C\mathbf{k}$. Substituting D for the constant $-Ax_1-By_1-Cz_1$, we write the equation in the form

$$Ax + By + Cz + D = 0. \tag{3}$$

Conversely, any linear equation of the form (3) represents a plane. Starting with this equation, we can find a point $P_1(x_1,y_1,z_1)$ whose coordinates satisfy it. Then we have

$$Ax_1 + By_1 + Cz_1 + D = 0.$$

This equation and equation (3) yield, by subtraction,

$$A(x - x_1) + B(y - y_1) + C(z - z_1) = 0,$$

which is of the form (2). Hence equation (3) represents a plane perpendicular to the vector $\mathbf{N} = A\mathbf{i} + B\mathbf{j} + C\mathbf{k}$.

THEOREM. *Any plane can be represented by a linear equation. Conversely, the locus of a linear equation is a plane.*

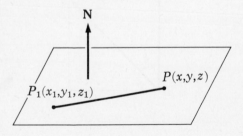

FIGURE 12–12

EXAMPLE 1. Write the equation of the plane which contains the point $P_1(4,-3,2)$ and is perpendicular to the vector $\mathbf{N} = 2\mathbf{i} - 3\mathbf{j} + 5\mathbf{k}$.

Solution. We use the coefficients of $\mathbf{i}$, $\mathbf{j}$, and $\mathbf{k}$ as the coefficients of x, y, and z and write the equation

$$2x - 3y + 5z + D = 0.$$

For any value of D this equation represents a plane perpendicular to the given vector. The equation will be satisfied by the coordinates of the given point if

$$8 + 9 + 10 + D = 0, \quad \text{or} \quad D = -27.$$

The required equation therefore is

$$2x - 3y + 5z - 27 = 0.$$

EXAMPLE 2. Find the equation of the plane determined by the points $P_1(1,2,6)$, $P_2(4,4,1)$, and $P_3(2,3,5)$.

Solution. A vector which is perpendicular to two sides of the triangle is normal to the plane of the triangle. To find such a vector, we write

$$\overrightarrow{P_1P_2} = 3\mathbf{i} + 2\mathbf{j} - 5\mathbf{k},$$
$$\overrightarrow{P_1P_3} = \mathbf{i} + \mathbf{j} - \mathbf{k},$$
$$\mathbf{N} = A\mathbf{i} + B\mathbf{j} + C\mathbf{k}.$$

The coefficients A, B, and C are to be found so that $\mathbf{N}$ is perpendicular to each of the other vectors. Thus

$$\mathbf{N} \cdot \overrightarrow{P_1P_2} = 3A + 2B - 5C = 0,$$
$$\mathbf{N} \cdot \overrightarrow{P_1P_3} = A + B - C = 0.$$

These equations give $A = 3C$ and $B = -2C$. Choosing $C = 1$, we have $\mathbf{N} = 3\mathbf{i} - 2\mathbf{j} + \mathbf{k}$. The plane $3x - 2y + z + D = 0$ is normal to $\mathbf{N}$, and passes through the given points if $D = -5$. Hence we have

$$3x - 2y + z - 5 = 0.$$

EXAMPLE 3. Find the distance d from the point $P(6,4,-1)$ to the plane $2x + 3y - 6z - 2 = 0$.

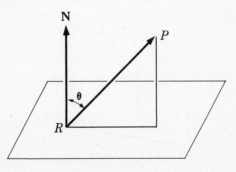

FIGURE 12–13

Solution. Let R be any point of the plane (Fig. 12–13). The scalar projection of the vector $\overrightarrow{RP}$ on a vector perpendicular to the plane gives the required distance. This scalar projection is obtained by taking the dot product of $\overrightarrow{RP}$ and a unit vector normal to the plane. The point $(1,0,0)$ is in the plane, and using this point for R, we have $\overrightarrow{RP} = 5\mathbf{i} + 4\mathbf{j} - \mathbf{k}$. Either of the vectors

$$\mathbf{N} = \pm\,\frac{2\mathbf{i} + 3\mathbf{j} - 6\mathbf{k}}{7}$$

is a unit vector normal to the plane. Hence

$$\mathbf{N} \cdot \overrightarrow{RP} = \pm\,\frac{10 + 12 + 6}{7} = \pm\,\frac{28}{7}.$$

We choose the ambiguous sign $+$ in order to have a positive result. Thus we get $d = 4$.

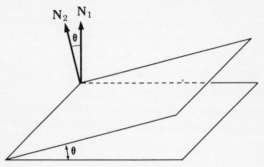

FIGURE 12–14

EXAMPLE 4. Find the angle θ between the planes $4x - 8y - z + 5 = 0$ and $x + 2y - 2z + 3 = 0$.

Solution. The angle between two planes is equal to the angle between their normals (Fig. 12–14). The vectors

$$\mathbf{N}_1 = \frac{4\mathbf{i} - 8\mathbf{j} - \mathbf{k}}{9}, \quad \mathbf{N}_2 = \frac{\mathbf{i} + 2\mathbf{j} - 2\mathbf{k}}{3}$$

are unit vectors normal to the given planes. The dot product yields

$$\cos\theta = \mathbf{N}_1 \cdot \mathbf{N}_2 = -\tfrac{10}{27}, \quad \text{and} \quad \theta = 112°.$$

The planes intersect, making a pair of angles equal (approximately) to 112°, and a second pair equal to 68°. Choosing the smaller angle, we give the angle between the planes as 68°.

EXERCISE 12–4

Write the equation of the plane which satisfies the given conditions in each problem 1–8.

1. Perpendicular to $\mathbf{N} = 3\mathbf{i} - 2\mathbf{j} + 5\mathbf{k}$ and passes through the point $(1,1,2)$.
2. Perpendicular to $\mathbf{N} = 4\mathbf{i} - \mathbf{j} - \mathbf{k}$ and passes through the origin.

3. Parallel to the plane $2x - 3y - 4z = 5$ and passes through $(1,2,-3)$.

4. Perpendicular to the line segment $(4,0,6)$, $(0,-8,2)$ at its mid-point.

5. Passes through the origin and is perpendicular to the line through $(2,-3,4)$ and $(5,6,0)$.

6. Passes through the points $(0,1,2)$, $(2,0,3)$, $(4,3,0)$.

7. Passes through the points $(2,-2,-1)$, $(-3,4,1)$, $(4,2,3)$.

8. Passes through $(0,0,0)$, $(3,0,0)$, $(1,1,1)$.

Find the distance from the given point to the given plane in each problem 9–12.

9. $2x - y + 2z + 3 = 0$; $(0,1,3)$.

10. $6x + 2y - 3z + 2 = 0$; $(2,-4,3)$.

11. $4x - 2y + z - 2 = 0$; $(-1,1,2)$.

12. $3x - 4y - 5z = 0$; $(5,-1,3)$.

Find the cosine of the acute angle between each pair of planes in problems 13–16.

13. $2x + y + z + 3 = 0$, $2x - 2y + z - 7 = 0$.

14. $2x + y + 2z - 5 = 0$, $2x - 3y + 6z + 5 = 0$.

15. $3x - 2y + z - 9 = 0$, $x - 3y - 9z + 4 = 0$.

16. $x - 8y + 4z - 3 = 0$, $4x + 2y - 4z + 3 = 0$.

17. Show that the planes

$$A_1x + B_1y + C_1z + D_1 = 0$$
$$A_2x + B_2y + C_2z + D_2 = 0$$

are perpendicular if and only if

$$A_1A_2 + B_1B_2 + C_1C_2 = 0.$$

18. Determine the value of C so that the planes $2x - 6y + Cz = 5$ and $x - 3y + 2z = 4$ are perpendicular.

19. Use vectors to show that the distance d from $P_1(x_1,y_1,z_1)$ to the plane $Ax + By + Cz + D = 0$ is

$$d = \frac{|Ax_1 + By_1 + Cz_1 + D|}{\sqrt{A^2 + B^2 + C^2}}.$$

12–7 The equations of a line. Let L be a line which passes through a given point $P_1(x_1,y_1,z_1)$ and is parallel to a given nonzero vector

$$\mathbf{V} = A\mathbf{i} + B\mathbf{j} + C\mathbf{k}.$$

If $P(x,y,z)$ is a point on the line, then the vector $\overrightarrow{P_1P}$ is parallel to $\mathbf{V}$ (Fig. 12–15).   Conversely, if $\overrightarrow{P_1P}$ is parallel to $\mathbf{V}$, the point P is on the line L.   Hence P is on L if and only if there is a scalar t such that

$$\overrightarrow{P_1P} = t\mathbf{V},$$

or

$$(x - x_1)\mathbf{i} + (y - y_1)\mathbf{j} + (z - z_1)\mathbf{k} = At\mathbf{i} + Bt\mathbf{j} + Ct\mathbf{k}. \tag{1}$$

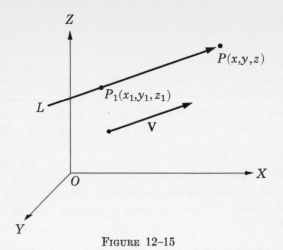

FIGURE 12–15

Equating corresponding coefficients of **i**, **j**, and **k**, we obtain the equations

$$x - x_1 = At, \quad y - y_1 = Bt, \quad z - z_1 = Ct,$$

or, transposing,

$$x = x_1 + At, \quad y = y_1 + Bt, \quad z = z_1 + Ct. \tag{2}$$

When t is given any real value, equations (2) determine the coordinates (x,y,z) of a point on the line L. Also there is a value of t corresponding to any point of the line. Equations (2) are called *parametric equations* of the line.

By solving each of the parametric equations for t and equating the equal values, we get

$$\frac{x - x_1}{A} = \frac{y - y_1}{B} = \frac{z - z_1}{C}. \tag{3}$$

These are called the *symmetric equations* of the line.

The planes which contain a line and are perpendicular to the coordinate planes are called *projecting planes*.

Equations (3) represent three projecting planes. This becomes evident when we write the equations as

$$\frac{x - x_1}{A} = \frac{y - y_1}{B}, \quad \frac{x - x_1}{A} = \frac{z - z_1}{C}, \quad \frac{y - y_1}{B} = \frac{z - z_1}{C}.$$

These equations, each in two variables, represent planes perpendicular respectively to the xy-, xz-, and yz-planes. These equations represent a line, and hence the line is the intersection of the planes. Any two of the equations, of course, determine the line. We notice also that any one of the equations can be obtained from the other two.

A line in space may be defined by two planes which pass through the line. Hence there are infinitely many ways of defining a line, since infinitely many planes pass through a line. However, it is usually convenient to deal with the projecting planes.

If a line is parallel to a coordinate plane, one of the quantities A, B, and C in equations (3) is zero, and conversely. In this case, one member of the equation would have zero in the denominator and could not be used. If, for example, $A = 0$ and B and C are not zero, then the line passing through $P_1(x_1, y_1, z_1)$ is parallel to the vector $\mathbf{V} = B\mathbf{j} + C\mathbf{k}$. Hence the line is parallel to the xy-plane and consequently the plane $x = x_1$ contains the line. If two of A, B, and C are zero, say $A = B = 0$, then the line is parallel to the z-axis. Hence the line is the intersection of the planes $x = x_1$ and $y = y_1$. Thus we see that when a denominator of a member of equations (3) is zero, the corresponding numerator equated to zero represents a plane through the line in question.

EXAMPLE 1. Write the equations of the line through $(2, -1, 3)$ which is parallel to the vector $\mathbf{V} = -2\mathbf{i} + 4\mathbf{j} + 6\mathbf{k}$.

Solution. The equations of the line in the symmetric form (3) are

$$\frac{x - 2}{-2} = \frac{y + 1}{4} = \frac{z - 3}{6}.$$

These equations in the parametric form (2) are

$$x = 2 - 2t, \quad y = -1 + 4t, \quad z = 3 + 6t.$$

EXAMPLE 2. A line passes through the points $P_1(2, -4, 5)$, $P_2(-1, 3, 1)$. Write its equations.

Solution. The vector from P_2 to P_1,

$$\overrightarrow{P_2P_1} = 3\mathbf{i} - 7\mathbf{j} + 4\mathbf{k},$$

is parallel to the line. Hence we get

$$\frac{x - 2}{3} = \frac{y + 4}{-7} = \frac{z - 5}{4}.$$

Had we used the vector $\overrightarrow{P_1P_2}$ instead of $\overrightarrow{P_2P_1}$, the signs would be reversed in all the denominators.

EXAMPLE 3. Find a symmetric form of the equations

$$x + y - z - 7 = 0, \quad x + 5y + 5z + 5 = 0.$$

Solution. We multiply the first equation by 5 and add to the second equation to eliminate z. We subtract the first equation from the second to eliminate x. This gives the equations

$$6x + 10y - 30 = 0 \quad \text{and} \quad 4y + 6z + 12 = 0.$$

By solving each of these for y, we obtain

$$y = \frac{-3x + 15}{5}, \quad y = \frac{-3z - 6}{2}.$$

Combining these equations and dividing by -3, we obtain the symmetric equations

$$\frac{x - 5}{5} = \frac{y}{-3} = \frac{z + 2}{2}.$$

EXAMPLE 4.   Write the equations of the line passing through the points $P_1(2,6,4)$ and $P_2(3,-2,4)$.

Solution.   The vector from P_1 to P_2 is

$$\overrightarrow{P_1P_2} = \mathbf{i} - 8\mathbf{j}.$$

Hence the required line is parallel to the xy-plane.   The plane $z = 4$ contains the line.   This plane is perpendicular to two of the coordinate planes.   We use the first two members of equations (3) to get another plane containing the line.   Thus we have the defining equations

$$z = 4, \quad \frac{x - 3}{1} = \frac{y + 2}{-8},$$

or

$$z = 4, \quad 8x + y - 22 = 0.$$

Notice that we could not use the third member of the symmetric equations because its denominator would be zero.   We did, however, set the numerator of that member equal to zero to obtain one of the planes.

EXAMPLE 5.   Find the equation of the line through $(2,-1,3)$ and parallel to the planes $2x - y + 4z - 5 = 0$ and $3x + y + z - 4 = 0$.

Solution.   Normals to the planes are given by the vectors

$$\mathbf{N}_1 = 2\mathbf{i} - \mathbf{j} + 4\mathbf{k},$$
$$\mathbf{N}_2 = 3\mathbf{i} + \mathbf{j} + \mathbf{k}.$$

The required line is perpendicular to these vectors.   Hence, if $\mathbf{V} = A\mathbf{i} + B\mathbf{j} + C\mathbf{k}$ is parallel to the line, we have

$$\mathbf{N}_1 \cdot \mathbf{V} = 2A - B + 4C = 0,$$
$$\mathbf{N}_2 \cdot \mathbf{V} = 3A + B + C = 0.$$

Solving these equations for A and B in terms of C, we get $A = -C$, $B = 2C$. Hence $\mathbf{V} = -C\mathbf{i} + 2C\mathbf{j} + C\mathbf{k}$.   Taking $C = 1$, then $\mathbf{V} = -\mathbf{i} + 2\mathbf{j} + \mathbf{k}$.   The equations of the line may therefore be written as

$$\frac{x - 2}{-1} = \frac{y + 1}{2} = \frac{z - 3}{1}.$$

12–8 Direction angles and direction cosines.

The angles, α, β, and γ which a directed line makes with the positive x-, y-, and z-axes respectively are called the *direction angles* of the line.   The cosines of the direction angles are called the *direction cosines* of the line. The direction cosines of a line represented by equations of the form (2) or (3) may be found by the use of vectors. The vector

$$\mathbf{V} = A\mathbf{i} + B\mathbf{j} + C\mathbf{k}$$

is parallel to the line. Having chosen one direction along the line as positive, then one of the vectors $\mathbf{V}$ or its negative points in the same direction as the line. The direction cosines are easily determined by using the dot product, as in problem 11, Exercise 12–3.

The angles formed by two lines which do not intersect are defined to be equal to the angles formed by two lines which do intersect and are parallel to the given lines. Hence vectors can be employed in finding the angles formed by two lines in space.

EXAMPLE. Assign a positive direction to the line represented by the equations

$$\frac{x - 1}{4} = \frac{y + 3}{-3} = \frac{z - 5}{-2}$$

and find the direction cosines.

Solution. The vectors $4\mathbf{i} - 3\mathbf{j} - 2\mathbf{k}$ and $-4\mathbf{i} + 3\mathbf{j} + 2\mathbf{k}$ are parallel to the line. We select the positive direction of the line upward, so that γ is an acute angle. Then the vector $\mathbf{V} = -4\mathbf{i} + 3\mathbf{j} + 2\mathbf{k}$ points in the positive direction of the line. Using the dot product, we get

$$\mathbf{i} \cdot \mathbf{V} = |\mathbf{i}|\,|\mathbf{V}| \cos \alpha,$$
$$-4 = \sqrt{29} \cos \alpha,$$
$$\cos \alpha = -\frac{4}{\sqrt{29}}.$$

Similarly, $\mathbf{j} \cdot \mathbf{V}$ and $\mathbf{k} \cdot \mathbf{V}$ yield $\cos \beta = \dfrac{3}{\sqrt{29}}$ and $\cos \gamma = \dfrac{2}{\sqrt{29}}$.

EXERCISE 12–5

Write a vector which is parallel to the line represented in each problem 1–4. By setting x, y, and z in turn equal to zero, find the points in which the line cuts the coordinate planes.

1. $\dfrac{x - 6}{2} = \dfrac{y + 2}{1} = \dfrac{z + 3}{3}.$ 2. $\dfrac{x}{-2} = \dfrac{y - 2}{1} = \dfrac{z - 3}{1}.$

3. $\dfrac{x - 3}{3} = \dfrac{y}{-1} = \dfrac{z - 4}{2}.$ 4. $\dfrac{x - 2}{1} = \dfrac{y + 1}{2} = \dfrac{z - 4}{3}.$

In each problem 5–14 write in two ways the equations of the line which passes through the given point and is parallel to the given vector.

5. $P(4, -3, 5); \; -2\mathbf{i} + 3\mathbf{j} + 4\mathbf{k}.$ 6. $P(0, 1, -2); \; \mathbf{i} - \mathbf{j} + 2\mathbf{k}.$

7. $P(1, 1, 2); \; 2\mathbf{i} + 3\mathbf{j} - \mathbf{k}.$ 8. $P(-2, -2, 3); \; 5\mathbf{i} + 4\mathbf{j} + \mathbf{k}.$

9. $P(2,-1,1)$; $2\mathbf{i} + \mathbf{j}$.   10. $P(3,3,3)$; $\mathbf{i} + \mathbf{k}$.

11. $P(4,3,2)$; $\mathbf{j} + 2\mathbf{k}$.   12. $P(0,0,0)$; $\mathbf{i}$.

13. $P(0,0,0)$; $\mathbf{j}$.   14. $P(0,0,0)$; $\mathbf{k}$.

Write the equations of the line through the two points in each problem 15–22.

15. $(1,2,3)$, $(-2,4,0)$.   16. $(0,0,0)$, $(3,4,5)$.

17. $(1,0,2)$, $(0,2,1)$.   18. $(2,4,0)$, $(1,2,8)$.

19. $(2,5,4)$, $(2,4,3)$.   20. $(0,4,3)$, $(0,4,4)$.

21. $(-1,3,4)$, $(3,3,4)$.   22. $(0,0,2)$, $(0,0,4)$

Find a symmetric form for each pair of equations in problems 23–26.

23. $x - y - 2z + 1 = 0$,
$x - 3y - 3z + 7 = 0$.   24. $x + y - 2z + 8 = 0$,
$2x - y - 2z + 4 = 0$.

25. $x + y + z - 9 = 0$,
$2x + y - z + 3 = 0$.   26. $x + y - z + 8 = 0$,
$2x - y + 2z + 6 = 0$.

27. Find the direction cosines of the lines defined in problems 1–4 of this exercise. In each case select the positive direction of the line so that γ is an acute angle.

Find the cosine of the acute angle formed by each pair of lines in problems 28–31.

28. $\dfrac{x - 1}{2} = \dfrac{y + 1}{1} = \dfrac{z - 3}{2}$, $\dfrac{x - 1}{2} = \dfrac{y + 1}{-2} = \dfrac{z - 3}{1}$.

29. $\dfrac{x + 2}{3} = \dfrac{y + 2}{6} = \dfrac{z}{2}$, $\dfrac{x - 1}{1} = \dfrac{y - 1}{2} = \dfrac{z - 4}{-2}$.

30. $x = 3 + t$, $y = 5 - 8t$, $z = 2 + 4t$;
$x = 3 + 4t$, $y = 5 - 2t$, $z = 2 - 4t$.

31. $x = t$, $y = -2t$, $z = 3t$;
$x = 6t$, $y = 4t$, $z = -2t$.

In each problem 32–34 find the equations of the line which passes through the given point and is parallel to each of the given planes.

32. $(0,0,0)$; $x - y + z = 4$, $x + y - 2z + 3 = 0$.

33. $(2,1,3)$; $2x - 3y + 2z = 5$, $3x + 2y - 2z = 7$.

34. $(-1,5,-5)$; $x - y = 5$, $y + z = 3$.

APPENDIX

TABLE I
Powers and Roots

No.	Sq.	Sq. Root	Cube	Cube Root	No.	Sq.	Sq. Root	Cube	Cube Root
1	1	1.000	1	1.000	51	2,601	7.141	132,651	3.708
2	4	1.414	8	1.260	52	2,704	7.211	140,608	3.733
3	9	1.732	27	1.442	53	2,809	7.280	148,877	3.756
4	16	2.000	64	1.587	54	2,916	7.348	157,464	3.780
5	25	2.236	125	1.710	55	3,025	7.416	166,375	3.803
6	36	2.449	216	1.817	56	3,136	7.483	175,616	3.826
7	49	2.646	343	1.913	57	3,249	7.550	185,193	3.849
8	64	2.828	512	2.000	58	3,364	7.616	195,112	3.871
9	81	3.000	729	2.080	59	3,481	7.681	205,379	3.893
10	100	3.162	1,000	2.154	60	3,600	7.746	216,000	3.915
11	121	3.317	1,331	2.224	61	3,721	7.810	226,981	3.936
12	144	3.464	1,728	2.289	62	3,844	7.874	238,328	3.958
13	169	3.606	2,197	2.351	63	3,969	7.937	250,047	3.979
14	196	3.742	2,744	2.410	64	4,096	8.000	262,144	4.000
15	225	3.873	3,375	2.466	65	4,225	8.062	274,625	4.021
16	256	4.000	4,096	2.520	66	4,356	8.124	287,496	4.041
17	289	4.123	4,913	2.571	67	4,489	8.185	300,763	4.062
18	324	4.243	5,832	2.621	68	4,624	8.246	314,432	4.082
19	361	4.359	6,859	2.668	69	4,761	8.307	328,509	4.102
20	400	4.472	8,000	2.714	70	4,900	8.367	343,000	4.121
21	441	4.583	9,261	2.759	71	5,041	8.426	357,911	4.141
22	484	4.690	10,648	2.802	72	5,184	8.485	373,248	4.160
23	529	4.796	12,167	2.844	73	5,329	8.544	389,017	4.179
24	576	4.899	13,824	2.884	74	5,476	8.602	405,224	4.198
25	625	5.000	15,625	2.924	75	5,625	8.660	421,875	4.217
26	676	5.099	17,576	2.962	76	5,776	8.718	438,976	4.236
27	729	5.196	19,683	3.000	77	5,929	8.775	456,533	4.254
28	784	5.292	21,952	3.037	78	6,084	8.832	474,552	4.273
29	841	5.385	24,389	3.072	79	6,241	8.888	493,039	4.291
30	900	5.477	27,000	3.107	80	6,400	8.944	512,000	4.309
31	961	5.568	29,791	3.141	81	6,561	9.000	531,441	4.327
32	1,024	5.657	32,768	3.175	82	6,724	9.055	551,368	4.344
33	1,089	5.745	35,937	3.208	83	6,889	9.110	571,787	4.362
34	1,156	5.831	39,304	3.240	84	7,056	9.165	592,704	4.380
35	1,225	5.916	42,875	3.271	85	7,225	9.220	614,125	4.397
36	1,296	6.000	46,656	3.302	86	7,396	9.274	636,056	4.414
37	1,369	6.083	50,653	3.332	87	7,569	9.327	658,503	4.431
38	1,444	6.164	54,872	3.362	88	7,744	9.381	681,472	4.448
39	1,521	6.245	59,319	3.391	89	7,921	9.434	704,969	4.465
40	1,600	6.325	64,000	3.420	90	8,100	9.487	729,000	4.481
41	1,681	6.403	68,921	3.448	91	8,281	9.539	753,571	4.498
42	1,764	6.481	74,088	3.476	92	8,464	9.592	778,688	4.514
43	1,849	6.557	79,507	3.503	93	8,649	9.644	804,357	4.531
44	1,936	6.633	85,184	3.530	94	8,836	9.695	830,584	4.547
45	2,025	6.708	91,125	3.557	95	9,025	9.747	857,375	4.563
46	2,116	6.782	97,336	3.583	96	9,216	9.798	884,736	4.579
47	2,209	6.856	103,823	3.609	97	9,409	9.849	912,673	4.595
48	2,304	6.928	110,592	3.634	98	9,604	9.899	941,192	4.610
49	2,401	7.000	117,649	3.659	99	9,801	9.950	970,299	4.626
50	2,500	7.071	125,000	3.684	100	10,000	10.000	1,000,000	4.642

TABLE II

Values of Trigonometric Functions (Degrees)

Angle	Sine	Cosine	Tangent	Angle	Sine	Cosine	Tangent
0°	0.000	1.000	0.000				
1°	.018	1.000	.018	46°	.719	.695	1.036
2°	.035	0.999	.035	47°	.731	.682	1.072
3°	.052	.999	.052	48°	.743	.669	1.111
4°	.070	.998	.070	49°	.755	.656	1.150
5°	.087	.996	.088	50°	.766	.643	1.192
6°	.105	.995	.105	51°	.777	.629	1.235
7°	.122	.993	.123	52°	.788	.616	1.280
8°	.139	.990	.141	53°	.799	.602	1.327
9°	.156	.988	.158	54°	.809	.588	1.376
10°	.174	.985	.176	55°	.819	.574	1.428
11°	.191	.982	.194	56°	.829	.559	1.483
12°	.208	.978	.213	57°	.839	.545	1.540
13°	.225	.974	.231	58°	.848	.530	1.600
14°	.242	.970	.249	59°	.857	.515	1.664
15°	.259	.966	.268	60°	.866	.500	1.732
16°	.276	.961	.287	61°	.875	.485	1.804
17°	.292	.956	.306	62°	.883	.470	1.881
18°	.309	.951	.325	63°	.891	.454	1.963
19°	.326	.946	.344	64°	.899	.438	2.050
20°	.342	.940	.364	65°	.906	.423	2.145
21°	.358	.934	.384	66°	.914	.407	2.246
22°	.375	.927	.404	67°	.921	.391	2.356
23°	.391	.921	.425	68°	.927	.375	2.475
24°	.407	.914	.445	69°	.934	.358	2.605
25°	.423	.906	.466	70°	.940	.342	2.747
26°	.438	.899	.488	71°	.946	.326	2.904
27°	.454	.891	.510	72°	.951	.309	3.078
28°	.470	.883	.532	73°	.956	.292	3.271
29°	.485	.875	.554	74°	.961	.276	3.487
30°	.500	.866	.577	75°	.966	.259	3.732
31°	.515	.857	.601	76°	.970	.242	4.011
32°	.530	.848	.625	77°	.974	.225	4.331
33°	.545	.839	.649	78°	.978	.208	4.705
34°	.559	.829	.675	79°	.982	.191	5.145
35°	.574	.819	.700	80°	.985	.174	5.671
36°	.588	.809	.727	81°	.988	.156	6.314
37°	.602	.799	.754	82°	.990	.139	7.115
38°	.616	.788	.781	83°	.993	.122	8.144
39°	.629	.777	.810	84°	.995	.105	9.514
40°	.643	.766	.839	85°	.996	.087	11.43
41°	.656	.755	.869	86°	.998	.070	14.30
42°	.669	.743	.900	87°	.999	.052	19.08
43°	.682	.731	.933	88°	.999	.035	28.64
44°	.695	.719	.966	89°	1.000	.018	57.29
45°	.707	.707	1.000	90°	1.000	.000	∞

TABLE III

Values of Trigonometric Functions (Radians)

Radians	Sin	Cos	Tan	Radians	Sin	Cos	Tan
.00	.0000	1.0000	.0000	.40	.3894	.9211	.4228
.01	.0100	1.0000	.0100	.41	.3986	.9171	.4346
.02	.0200	.9998	.0200	.42	.4078	.9131	.4466
.03	.0300	.9996	.0300	.43	.4169	.9090	.4586
.04	.0400	.9992	.0400	.44	.4259	.9048	.4708
.05	.0500	.9988	.0500	.45	.4350	.9004	.4831
.06	.0600	.9982	.0601	.46	.4439	.8961	.4954
.07	.0699	.9976	.0701	.47	.4529	.8916	.5080
.08	.0799	.9968	.0802	.48	.4618	.8870	.5206
.09	.0899	.9960	.0902	.49	.4706	.8823	.5334
.10	.0998	.9950	.1003	.50	.4794	.8776	.5463
.11	.1098	.9940	.1104	.51	.4882	.8727	.5594
.12	.1197	.9928	.1206	.52	.4969	.8678	.5726
.13	.1296	.9916	.1307	.53	.5055	.8628	.5859
.14	.1395	.9902	.1409	.54	.5141	.8577	.5994
.15	.1494	.9888	.1511	.55	.5227	.8525	.6131
.16	.1593	.9872	.1614	.56	.5312	.8473	.6269
.17	.1692	.9856	.1717	.57	.5396	.8419	.6410
.18	.1790	.9838	.1820	.58	.5480	.8365	.6552
.19	.1889	.9820	.1923	.59	.5564	.8309	.6696
.20	.1987	.9801	.2027	.60	.5646	.8253	.6841
.21	.2085	.9780	.2131	.61	.5729	.8196	.6989
.22	.2182	.9759	.2236	.62	.5810	.8139	.7139
.23	.2280	.9737	.2341	.63	.5891	.8080	.7291
.24	.2377	.9713	.2447	.64	.5972	.8021	.7445
.25	.2474	.9689	.2553	.65	.6052	.7961	.7602
.26	.2571	.9664	.2660	.66	.6131	.7900	.7761
.27	.2667	.9638	.2768	.67	.6210	.7838	.7923
.28	.2764	.9611	.2876	.68	.6288	.7776	.8087
.29	.2860	.9582	.2984	.69	.6365	.7712	.8253
.30	.2955	.9553	.3093	.70	.6442	.7648	.8423
.31	.3051	.9523	.3203	.71	.6518	.7584	.8595
.32	.3146	.9492	.3314	.72	.6594	.7518	.8771
.33	.3240	.9460	.3425	.73	.6669	.7452	.8949
.34	.3335	.9428	.3537	.74	.6743	.7385	.9131
.35	.3429	.9394	.3650	.75	.6816	.7317	.9316
.36	.3523	.9359	.3764	.76	.6889	.7248	.9505
.37	.3616	.9323	.3879	.77	.6961	.7179	.9697
.38	.3709	.9287	.3994	.78	.7033	.7109	.9893
.39	.3802	.9249	.4111	.79	.7104	.7038	1.009

(cont'd)

TABLE III (cont.)

Values of Trigonometric Functions (Radians)

Radians	Sin	Cos	Tan	Radians	Sin	Cos	Tan
.80	.7174	.6967	1.030	1.20	.9320	.3624	2.572
.81	.7243	.6895	1.050	1.21	.9356	.3530	2.650
.82	.7311	.6822	1.072	1.22	.9391	.3436	2.733
.83	.7379	.6749	1.093	1.23	.9425	.3342	2.820
.84	.7446	.6675	1.116	1.24	.9458	.3248	2.912
.85	.7513	.6600	1.138	1.25	.9490	.3153	3.010
.86	.7578	.6524	1.162	1.26	.9521	.3058	3.113
.87	.7643	.6448	1.185	1.27	.9551	.2963	3.224
.88	.7707	.6372	1.210	1.28	.9580	.2867	3.341
.89	.7771	.6294	1.235	1.29	.9608	.2771	3.467
.90	.7833	.6216	1.260	1.30	.9636	.2675	3.602
.91	.7895	.6137	1.286	1.31	.9662	.2579	3.747
.92	.7956	.6058	1.313	1.32	.9687	.2482	3.903
.93	.8016	.5978	1.341	1.33	.9711	.2385	4.072
.94	.8076	.5898	1.369	1.34	.9735	.2288	4.256
.95	.8134	.5817	1.398	1.35	.9757	.2190	4.455
.96	.8192	.5735	1.428	1.36	.9779	.2092	4.673
.97	.8249	.5653	1.459	1.37	.9799	.1995	4.913
.98	.8305	.5570	1.491	1.38	.9819	.1896	5.177
.99	.8360	.5487	1.524	1.39	.9837	.1798	5.471
1.00	.8415	.5403	1.557	1.40	.9854	.1700	5.798
1.01	.8468	.5319	1.592	1.41	.9871	.1601	6.165
1.02	.8521	.5234	1.628	1.42	.9887	.1502	6.581
1.03	.8573	.5148	1.665	1.43	.9901	.1403	7.055
1.04	.8624	.5062	1.704	1.44	.9915	.1304	7.602
1.05	.8674	.4976	1.743	1.45	.9927	.1205	8.238
1.06	.8724	.4889	1.784	1.46	.9939	.1106	8.989
1.07	.8772	.4801	1.827	1.47	.9949	.1006	9.887
1.08	.8820	.4713	1.871	1.48	.9959	.0907	10.98
1.09	.8866	.4625	1.917	1.49	.9967	.0807	12.35
1.10	.8912	.4536	1.965	1.50	.9975	.0707	14.10
1.11	.8957	.4447	2.014	1.51	.9982	.0608	16.43
1.12	.9001	.4357	2.066	1.52	.9987	.0508	19.67
1.13	.9044	.4267	2.120	1.53	.9992	.0408	24.50
1.14	.9086	.4176	2.176	1.54	.9995	.0308	32.46
1.15	.9128	.4085	2.234	1.55	.9998	.0208	48.08
1.16	.9168	.3993	2.296	1.56	.9999	.0108	92.62
1.17	.9208	.3902	2.360	1.57	1.000	.0008	1256.
1.18	.9246	.3809	2.427				
1.19	.9284	.3717	2.498				

TABLE IV

Exponential Functions

x	e^x	e^{-x}	x	e^x	e^{-x}
.00	1.0000	1.0000	2.5	12.182	.0821
.05	1.0513	.9512	2.6	13.464	.0743
.10	1.1052	.9048	2.7	14.880	.0672
.15	1.1618	.8607	2.8	16.445	.0608
.20	1.2214	.8187	2.9	18.174	.0550
.25	1.2840	.7788	3.0	20.086	.0498
.30	1.3499	.7408	3.1	22.198	.0450
.35	1.4191	.7047	3.2	24.533	.0408
.40	1.4918	.6703	3.3	27.113	.0369
.45	1.5683	.6376	3.4	29.964	.0334
.50	1.6487	.6065	3.5	33.115	.0302
.55	1.7333	.5769	3.6	36.598	.0273
.60	1.8221	.5488	3.7	40.447	.0247
.65	1.9155	.5220	3.8	44.701	.0224
.70	2.0138	.4966	3.9	49.402	.0202
.75	2.1170	.4724	4.0	54.598	.0183
.80	2.2255	.4493	4.1	60.340	.0166
.85	2.3396	.4274	4.2	66.686	.0150
.90	2.4596	.4066	4.3	73.700	.0136
.95	2.5857	.3867	4.4	81.451	.0123
1.0	2.7183	.3679	4.5	90.017	.0111
1.1	3.0042	.3329	4.6	99.484	.0101
1.2	3.3201	.3012	4.7	109.95	.0091
1.3	3.6693	.2725	4.8	121.51	.0082
1.4	4.0552	.2466	4.9	134.29	.0074
1.5	4.4817	.2231	5	148.41	.0067
1.6	4.9530	.2019	6	403.43	.0025
1.7	5.4739	.1827	7	1096.6	.0009
1.8	6.0496	.1653	8	2981.0	.0003
1.9	6.6859	.1496	9	8103.1	.0001
2.0	7.3891	.1353	10	22026.	.0000
2.1	8.1662	.1225			
2.2	9.0250	.1108			
2.3	9.9742	.1003			
2.4	11.023	.0907			

TABLE V

Common Logarithms of Numbers

N	0	1	2	3	4	5	6	7	8	9
10	0000	0043	0086	0128	0170	0212	0253	0294	0334	0374
11	0414	0453	0492	0531	0569	0607	0645	0682	0719	0755
12	0792	0828	0864	0899	0934	0969	1004	1038	1072	1106
13	1139	1173	1206	1239	1271	1303	1335	1367	1399	1430
14	1461	1492	1523	1553	1584	1614	1644	1673	1703	1732
15	1761	1790	1818	1847	1875	1903	1931	1959	1987	2014
16	2041	2068	2095	2122	2148	2175	2201	2227	2253	2279
17	2304	2330	2355	2380	2405	2430	2455	2480	2504	2529
18	2553	2577	2601	2625	2648	2672	2695	2718	2742	2765
19	2788	2810	2833	2856	2878	2900	2923	2945	2967	2989
20	3010	3032	3054	3075	3096	3118	3139	3160	3181	3201
21	3222	3243	3263	3284	3304	3324	3345	3365	3385	3404
22	3424	3444	3464	3483	3502	3522	3541	3560	3579	3598
23	3617	3636	3655	3674	3692	3711	3729	3747	3766	3784
24	3802	3820	3838	3856	3874	3892	3909	3927	3945	3962
25	3979	3997	4014	4031	4048	4065	4082	4099	4116	4133
26	4150	4166	4183	4200	4216	4232	4249	4265	4281	4298
27	4314	4330	4346	4362	4378	4393	4409	4425	4440	4456
28	4472	4487	4502	4518	4533	4548	4564	4579	4594	4609
29	4624	4639	4654	4669	4683	4698	4713	4728	4742	4757
30	4771	4786	4800	4814	4829	4843	4857	4871	4886	4900
31	4914	4928	4942	4955	4969	4983	4997	5011	5024	5038
32	5051	5065	5079	5092	5105	5119	5132	5145	5159	5172
33	5185	5198	5211	5224	5237	5250	5263	5276	5289	5302
34	5315	5328	5340	5353	5366	5378	5391	5403	5416	5428
35	5441	5453	5465	5478	5490	5502	5514	5527	5539	5551
36	5563	5575	5587	5599	5611	5623	5635	5647	5658	5670
37	5682	5694	5705	5717	5729	5740	5752	5763	5775	5786
38	5798	5809	5821	5832	5843	5855	5866	5877	5888	5899
39	5911	5922	5933	5944	5955	5966	5977	5988	5999	6010
40	6021	6031	6042	6053	6064	6075	6085	6096	6107	6117
41	6128	6138	6149	6160	6170	6180	6191	6201	6212	6222
42	6232	6243	6253	6263	6274	6284	6294	6304	6314	6325
43	6335	6345	6355	6365	6375	6385	6395	6405	6415	6425
44	6435	6444	6454	6464	6474	6484	6493	6503	6513	6522
45	6532	6542	6551	6561	6571	6580	6590	6599	6609	6618
46	6628	6637	6646	6656	6665	6675	6684	6693	6702	6712
47	6721	6730	6739	6749	6758	6767	6776	6785	6794	6803
48	6812	6821	6830	6839	6848	6857	6866	6875	6884	6893
49	6902	6911	6920	6928	6937	6946	6955	6964	6972	6981
50	6990	6998	7007	7016	7024	7033	7042	7050	7059	7067
51	7076	7084	7093	7101	7110	7118	7126	7135	7143	7152
52	7160	7168	7177	7185	7193	7202	7210	7218	7226	7235
53	7243	7251	7259	7267	7275	7284	7292	7300	7308	7316
54	7324	7332	7340	7348	7356	7364	7372	7380	7388	7396

TABLE V (cont.)

Common Logarithms of Numbers

N	0	1	2	3	4	5	6	7	8	9
55	7404	7412	7419	7427	7435	7443	7451	7459	7466	7474
56	7482	7490	7497	7505	7513	7520	7528	7536	7543	7551
57	7559	7566	7574	7582	7589	7597	7604	7612	7619	7627
58	7634	7642	7649	7657	7664	7672	7679	7686	7694	7701
59	7709	7716	7723	7731	7738	7745	7752	7760	7767	7774
60	7782	7789	7796	7803	7810	7818	7825	7832	7839	7846
61	7853	7860	7868	7875	7882	7889	7896	7903	7910	7917
62	7924	7931	7938	7945	7952	7959	7966	7973	7980	7987
63	7993	8000	8007	8014	8021	8028	8035	8041	8048	8055
64	8062	8069	8075	8082	8089	8096	8102	8109	8116	8122
65	8129	8136	8142	8149	8156	8162	8169	8176	8182	8189
66	8195	8202	8209	8215	8222	8228	8235	8241	8248	8254
67	8261	8267	8274	8280	8287	8293	8299	8306	8312	8319
68	8325	8331	8338	8344	8351	8357	8363	8370	8376	8382
69	8388	8395	8401	8407	8414	8420	8426	8432	8439	8445
70	8451	8457	8463	8470	8476	8482	8488	8494	8500	8506
71	8513	8519	8525	8531	8537	8543	8549	8555	8561	8567
72	8573	8579	8585	8591	8597	8603	8609	8615	8621	8627
73	8633	8639	8645	8651	8657	8663	8669	8675	8681	8686
74	8692	8698	8704	8710	8716	8722	8727	8733	8739	8745
75	8751	8756	8762	8768	8774	8779	8785	8791	8797	8802
76	8808	8814	8820	8825	8831	8837	8842	8848	8854	8859
77	8865	8871	8876	8882	8887	8893	8899	8904	8910	8915
78	8921	8927	8932	8938	8943	8949	8954	8960	8965	8971
79	8976	8982	8987	8993	8998	9004	9009	9015	9020	9025
80	9031	9036	9042	9047	9053	9058	9063	9069	9074	9079
81	9085	9090	9096	9101	9106	9112	9117	9122	9128	9133
82	9138	9143	9149	9154	9159	9165	9170	9175	9180	9186
83	9191	9196	9201	9206	9212	9217	9222	9227	9232	9238
84	9243	9248	9253	9258	9263	9269	9274	9279	9284	9289
85	9294	9299	9304	9309	9315	9320	9325	9330	9335	9340
86	9345	9350	9355	9360	9365	9370	9375	9380	9385	9390
87	9395	9400	9405	9410	9415	9420	9425	9430	9435	9440
88	9445	9450	9455	9460	9465	9469	9474	9479	9484	9489
89	9494	9499	9504	9509	9513	9518	9523	9528	9533	9538
90	9542	9547	9552	9557	9562	9566	9571	9576	9581	9586
91	9590	9595	9600	9605	9609	9614	9619	9624	9628	9633
92	9638	9643	9647	9652	9657	9661	9666	9671	9675	9680
93	9685	9689	9694	9699	9703	9708	9713	9717	9722	9727
94	9731	9736	9741	9745	9750	9754	9759	9763	9768	9773
95	9777	9782	9786	9791	9795	9800	9805	9809	9814	9818
96	9823	9827	9832	9836	9841	9845	9850	9854	9859	9863
97	9868	9872	9877	9881	9886	9890	9894	9899	9903	9908
98	9912	9917	9921	9926	9930	9934	9939	9943	9948	9952
99	9956	9961	9965	9969	9974	9978	9983	9987	9991	9996

TABLE VI

Natural Logarithms of Numbers

n	$\log_e n$	n	$\log_e n$	n	$\log_e n$
0.0	*	4.5	1.5041	9.0	2.1972
0.1	7.6974	4.6	1.5261	9.1	2.2083
0.2	8.3906	4.7	1.5476	9.2	2.2192
0.3	8.7960	4.8	1.5686	9.3	2.2300
0.4	9.0837	4.9	1.5892	9.4	2.2407
0.5	9.3069	5.0	1.6094	9.5	2.2513
0.6	9.4892	5.1	1.6292	9.6	2.2618
0.7	9.6433	5.2	1.6487	9.7	2.2721
0.8	9.7769	5.3	1.6677	9.8	2.2824
0.9	9.8946	5.4	1.6864	9.9	2.2925
1.0	0.0000	5.5	1.7047	10	2.3026
1.1	0.0953	5.6	1.7228	11	2.3979
1.2	0.1823	5.7	1.7405	12	2.4849
1.3	0.2624	5.8	1.7579	13	2.5649
1.4	0.3365	5.9	1.7750	14	2.6391
1.5	0.4055	6.0	1.7918	15	2.7081
1.6	0.4700	6.1	1.8083	16	2.7726
1.7	0.5306	6.2	1.8245	17	2.8332
1.8	0.5878	6.3	1.8405	18	2.8904
1.9	0.6419	6.4	1.8563	19	2.9444
2.0	0.6931	6.5	1.8718	20	2.9957
2.1	0.7419	6.6	1.8871	25	3.2189
2.2	0.7885	6.7	1.9021	30	3.4012
2.3	0.8329	6.8	1.9169	35	3.5553
2.4	0.8755	6.9	1.9315	40	3.6889
2.5	0.9163	7.0	1.9459	45	3.8067
2.6	0.9555	7.1	1.9601	50	3.9120
2.7	0.9933	7.2	1.9741	55	4.0073
2.8	1.0296	7.3	1.9879	60	4.0943
2.9	1.0647	7.4	2.0015	65	4.1744
3.0	1.0986	7.5	2.0149	70	4.2485
3.1	1.1314	7.6	2.0281	75	4.3175
3.2	1.1632	7.7	2.0412	80	4.3820
3.3	1.1939	7.8	2.0541	85	4.4427
3.4	1.2238	7.9	2.0669	90	4.4998
3.5	1.2528	8.0	2.0794	95	4.5539
3.6	1.2809	8.1	2.0919	100	4.6052
3.7	1.3083	8.2	2.1041		
3.8	1.3350	8.3	2.1163		
3.9	1.3610	8.4	2.1282		
4.0	1.3863	8.5	2.1401		
4.1	1.4110	8.6	2.1518		
4.2	1.4351	8.7	2.1633		
4.3	1.4586	8.8	2.1748		
4.4	1.4816	8.9	2.1861		

* Deduct 10 from each of the first nine values in column two.

ANSWERS TO ODD–NUMBERED PROBLEMS

EXERCISE 1–1

5. (a) On the x-axis; (b) on the y-axis.

7. (a) On a line bisecting the first and third quadrants; (b) on a line bisecting the second and fourth quadrants. 9. $(0, 3\sqrt{3})$, $9\sqrt{3}$ square units.

EXERCISE 1–2

1. (a) All real values except 2 and -3; (b) $0 \leq x \leq 1$; (c) $3 \leq x < 4, x > 4$.

3. (a) $y = \pm 2\sqrt{x}, x = \frac{1}{4}y^2$; $x \geq 0$, $-\infty < y < \infty$ (i.e., all real values). (b) $y = 5/x$, $x = 5/y$; each variable may take any real value except zero. (c) $y = \pm\sqrt{x^2 - 9}$; $x = \pm\sqrt{y^2 + 9}$; $|x| \geq 3$ (i.e., the numerical value of x is equal to or greater than 3), $-\infty < y < \infty$.

5. $1, -1, s^3 - s^2 + 1$. 7. $4t + 3, 2t + 5, 2t^2 + 3$.

9. $F(2x) = \dfrac{2x - 1}{2x + 1}$, $F(x - 3) = \dfrac{x - 4}{x - 2}$, $F\left(\dfrac{1}{x}\right) = \dfrac{1 - x}{1 + x}$.

EXERCISE 1–5

1. $(3,2)$. 3. $(2,3), (-2,-3)$. 5. $(1,2), (-1,-2)$.

7. $(0,0), (2,8), (-2,-8)$.

9. $(\frac{5}{2}\sqrt{2}, \pm\frac{1}{2}\sqrt{14}), (-\frac{5}{2}\sqrt{2}, \pm\frac{1}{2}\sqrt{14})$. 11. $(3 \pm \sqrt{5}, 2 \pm 2\sqrt{5})$.

EXERCISE 2–1

1. $AB = 2, AC = 6, BC = 4, BA = -2, CA = -6, CB = -4$.

5. 13. 7. 13. 9. $3\sqrt{2}$. 11. $\sqrt{5}, \sqrt{10}, \sqrt{13}$. 13. $1, 3\sqrt{2}, 5$. 29. $(0,-2)$.

EXERCISE 2–2

1. (a) 1; (b) 0; (c) $\sqrt{3}$; (d) $-\sqrt{3}$; (e) -1. 3. -3. 5. $\frac{3}{4}$. 7. $\frac{13}{12}$.

13. $\tan A = 5, A = 79°$; $\tan B = 8, B = 83°$; $\tan C = \frac{1}{3}, C = 18°$.

15. $\tan A = 1, A = 45°$; $\tan B = 1, B = 45°$; $C = 90°$, and has no tangent.

17. $\frac{1}{3}$ or -3.

EXERCISE 2–3

1. (a) $(1,-1)$; (b) $(2,3)$; (c) $(2,6)$; (d) $(\frac{3}{2}, \frac{3}{2})$.

3. $(\frac{3}{2},3)$, the segments bisect each other. 5. $(-1,4), (3,2)$.

7. $(\frac{2}{3},2), (\frac{7}{3},4)$. 9. $(4,1)$, the same for each median.

11. $(\frac{13}{2}, \frac{19}{2}), (-\frac{15}{2}, -\frac{9}{2})$. 13. $r = 2$. 15. $r = 3$.

EXERCISE 3–1

1. $y = -3x + 6$; $m = -3, b = 6$. 3. $y = 2x - \frac{3}{2}$; $m = 2, b = -\frac{3}{2}$.

5. $y = -\frac{1}{2}x - 2$; $m = -\frac{1}{2}, b = -2$. 7. $y = \frac{4}{3}x$; $m = \frac{4}{3}, b = 0$.

9. $y = -\frac{5}{3}x + \frac{7}{3}$; $m = -\frac{5}{3}, b = \frac{7}{3}$. 11. $y = \frac{7}{11}x - \frac{9}{11}$; $m = \frac{7}{11}, b = -\frac{9}{11}$.

13. $m = 4, a = 3, b = -12$. 15. $m = -1, a = -4, b = -4$.

17. $m = \frac{3}{4}, a = 4, b = -3$. 19. $m = -\frac{1}{7}, a = 11, b = \frac{11}{7}$.

21. $m = -\frac{7}{3}, a = -\frac{6}{7}, b = -2$. 23. $m = -\frac{8}{3}, a = \frac{1}{2}, b = \frac{4}{3}$.

25. $y = 3x - 4$. 27. $y = -4x + 5$. 29. $2x - 3y = 6$.

31. $y = -6$. 33. $7x + 2y + 16 = 0$. 35. $y = 0$.

EXERCISE 3–1 cont'd.

37. $2x + 3y = 6$.   39. $3x - 4y = 12$.   41. $x + y + 2 = 0$.

43. $3x + 4y = 2$.   45. $21x + 22y = 77$.   47. $33x + 4y + 22 = 0$.

49. $2x - y = 5$.   51. $2x - 3y + 4 = 0$.   53. $x + 2y + 15 = 0$.

55. $y = 3$.   57. $8x + 3y = 0$.   59. $6x + y + 37 = 0$.

61. $6x + 7y = 11$.   63. $2x + y - 2 = 0$.   65. $x = 3$.

67. $8x - 27y = 58$.   69. $x = 0$.   71. $2x - y + 1 = 0$.

75. $2x - 3y = 5, 3x + 2y = 14$.   77. $7x + 5y - 41 = 0, 5x - 7y + 13 = 0$.

79. $8x - y - 19 = 0, x + 8y + 22 = 0$.   81. $y = 1, x = -1$.

83. $9x + y - 63 = 0, x - 9y - 7 = 0$.

85. (a) $x - 4y - 1 = 0, 3x - y = 3, 2x + 3y = 24$.

   (b) $4x - 5y = 4, x + 7y = 23, 5x + 2y = 27$; $(\frac{13}{3}, \frac{8}{3})$.

   (c) $3x - 2y = 3, x + 3y = 15, 4x + y = 18$; $(\frac{39}{11}, \frac{42}{11})$.

   (d) $4x + y = 21, x + 3y = 11, 3x - 2y = 10$; $(\frac{52}{11}, \frac{23}{11})$.

EXERCISE 3–2

1. $\frac{99}{13}$.   3. $3\sqrt{2}$.   5. $-\dfrac{5\sqrt{29}}{29}$.   7. 3.

9. 5.   11. $7x - 4y = D$.   13. $x + 2y = 2b$.   15. $4x - ay = 4a$.

17. $x - 2y + 7 + k(5x - 7y - 3) = 0$.   19. All pass through $(0,4)$.

21. All have the slope $-\frac{9}{2}$.   23. All pass through $(0,3)$.

25. All pass through the point of intersection of $4x - 7y - 7 = 0$ and $y = 0$.

27. The equations in order, omitting problems 22 and 25, are: $4x + 3y - 12 = 0$, $y = 2x - 6$, $9x + 2y = 27$, $x + y = 3$, $7x + 3y = 21$, $3x + 82y - 9 = 0$. No line of the family of problem 22 or of problem 25 passes through $(3,0)$. Why?

29. $9x - 32y + 19 = 0$.   31. $34x - 55 = 0$.   33. $24x + 24y + 5 = 0$.

35. $20x + 25y + 62 = 0, 7x - 7y - 16 = 0, 27x + 18y + 46 = 0$.

37. $x - y = 5, 3x + 3y + 1 = 0$.

EXERCISE 4–1

1. $3x' + 2y' = 0$.   3. $y'^2 = 6x'$.

5. $x'^2 + y'^2 = 4$.   7. $x'y' = 11$.

9. $(1,2), x'^2 + y'^2 = 9$.   11. $(3,2), x'y' = 14$.

13. $(-3, -1), x'^2 + 2y'^2 = 9$.   15. $(1,3), y'^2 + 4x' = 0$.

17. $(-2, -2), y'^2 + 10x' = 0$.

EXERCISE 4–2

1. $y' + 2 = 0$.   3. $x'^2 - y'^2 = 8$.   5. $3x'^2 + y'^2 = 2$.

7. $y'^2 - 4x' = 0$.   9. $45°$.   11. $22\frac{1}{2}°$.

EXERCISE 4–3

1. $3x' - 4y' = 0$.   3. $\theta = \arctan \frac{3}{4}, 5y' + 6 = 0$.

5. $\theta = 45°, y'^2 - 4y' - 4x' - 4 = 0$.   Then a translation yields $y''^2 - 4x'' = 0$.

7. $\theta = \arctan \frac{4}{3}, x'^2 + 4y'^2 + 4x' - 16y' + 16 = 0$.   Then a translation gives $x''^2 + 4y''^2 = 4$.

11. $(x + 3)^2 = 0$, two coincident lines.

13. $(x + \frac{1}{2} - \frac{1}{2}\sqrt{3}i)(x + \frac{1}{2} + \frac{1}{2}\sqrt{3}i) = 0$, no graph.

EXERCISE 5-1

1. $F(1,0)$; ends of latus rectum $(1,-2)$, $(1,2)$; directrix $x = -1$.
3. $F(0,-\frac{5}{2})$; ends of latus rectum $(-5,-\frac{5}{2})$, $(5,-\frac{5}{2})$; directrix $y = \frac{5}{2}$.
5. $F(-\frac{3}{4},0)$; ends of latus rectum $(-\frac{3}{4},-\frac{3}{2})$, $(-\frac{3}{4},\frac{3}{2})$; directrix $4x = 3$.
7. $y^2 = 12x$.   9. $y^2 = 24x$.   11. $x^2 = -12y$.
13. $3x^2 + 16y = 0$.   15. $y^2 = -x$.   17. $x^2 = 400y$.

EXERCISE 5-2

1. $F(0,\pm4)$; $V(0,\pm5)$; $B(\pm3,0)$; $(\pm\frac{9}{5},-4)$, $(\pm\frac{9}{5},4)$.
3. $F(\pm5,0)$; $V(\pm13,0)$; $B(0,\pm12)$; $(-5,\pm\frac{144}{13})$, $(5,\pm\frac{144}{13})$.
5. $F(\pm2\sqrt{6},0)$; $V(\pm7,0)$; $B(0,\pm5)$; $(2\sqrt{6},\pm\frac{25}{7})$, $(-2\sqrt{6},\pm\frac{25}{7})$.
7. $F(0,\pm\sqrt{21})$; $V(0,\pm5)$; $B(\pm2,0)$; $(\pm\frac{4}{5},-\sqrt{21})$, $(\pm\frac{4}{5},\sqrt{21})$.
9. $F(0,\pm\sqrt{3})$; $V(0,\pm2)$; $B(\pm1,0)$; $(\pm\frac{1}{2},-\sqrt{3})$, $(\pm\frac{1}{2},\sqrt{3})$.

11. $\dfrac{x^2}{16} + \dfrac{y^2}{9} = 1$.   13. $\dfrac{y^2}{20} + \dfrac{x^2}{4} = 1$.   15. $\dfrac{x^2}{36} + \dfrac{y^2}{27} = 1$.

17. $\dfrac{x^2}{54} + \dfrac{y^2}{30} = 1$.   19. $\dfrac{y^2}{100} + \dfrac{x^2}{75} = 1$.   21. $\dfrac{x^2}{36} + \dfrac{y^2}{9} = 1$.

23. $\dfrac{x^2}{64} + \dfrac{y^2}{16} = 1$.   25. 91.4 and 94.6 million miles.

EXERCISE 5-3

1. $V(\pm4,0)$; $F(\pm5,0)$; $\dfrac{9}{2}$; $\dfrac{x}{4} - \dfrac{y}{3} = 0$, $\dfrac{x}{4} + \dfrac{y}{3} = 0$.

3. $V(0,\pm3)$; $F(0,\pm\sqrt{13})$; $\dfrac{8}{3}$; $\dfrac{y}{3} - \dfrac{x}{2} = 0$, $\dfrac{y}{3} + \dfrac{x}{2} = 0$.

5. $V(\pm2,0)$; $F(\pm5,0)$; 21; $\dfrac{x}{2} + \dfrac{y}{\sqrt{21}} = 0$, $\dfrac{x}{2} - \dfrac{y}{\sqrt{21}} = 0$.

7. $V(0,\pm6)$; $F(0,\pm 6\sqrt{2})$; 12; $x + y = 0$, $x - y = 0$.

9. $\dfrac{x^2}{16} - \dfrac{y^2}{9} = 1$.   11. $\dfrac{y^2}{21} - \dfrac{x^2}{4} = 1$.   13. $\dfrac{x^2}{4} - \dfrac{y^2}{5} = 1$.   15. $\dfrac{x^2}{16} - \dfrac{y^2}{20} = 1$.

EXERCISE 5-4

1. $(x - 2)^2 + (y + 6)^2 = 25$.   3. $x^2 + (y - 4)^2 = 16$.
5. $(x - 4)^2 + (y + 3)^2 = 25$.   7. $(y - 4)^2 = 12(x + 1)$.
9. $(x + \frac{3}{2})^2 = 4(y - 2)$.   11. $(y - 3)^2 = 12(x - 2)$.   13. $x^2 = \pm16(y - 2)$.
15. $\dfrac{(x - 5)^2}{25} + \dfrac{(y - 4)^2}{16} = 1$. Center $(5,4)$; $V'(0,4)$, $V(10,4)$; $F'(2,4)$, $F(8,4)$;
$B'(5,0)$, $B(5,8)$.
17. $\dfrac{(y + 3)^2}{3} + \dfrac{(x - 4)^2}{2} = 1$. Center $(4,-3)$; $V'(4,-3-\sqrt{3})$, $V(4,-3+\sqrt{3})$;
$F'(4,-4)$, $F(4,-2)$; $B'(4 - \sqrt{2},-3)$, $B(4 + \sqrt{2},-3)$.
19. $\dfrac{(y - 1)^2}{9} + \dfrac{(x - 5)^2}{4} = 1$.   21. $\dfrac{(x + 1)^2}{13} + \dfrac{(y + 1)^2}{9} = 1$.

23. $\dfrac{(x - 3)^2}{16} - \dfrac{y^2}{9} = 1$. $C(3,0)$; $V'(-1,0)$, $V(7,0)$; $F'(-2,0)$, $F(8,0)$.

EXERCISE 5–4 cont'd.

25. $\dfrac{(y-3)^2}{16} - \dfrac{(x+4)^2}{20} = 1.$ $C(-4,3)$; $V'(-4,-1)$, $V(-4,7)$; $F'(-4,-3)$, $F(-4,9)$.

27. $\dfrac{(x-1)^2}{9} - \dfrac{(y-3)^2}{4} = 1.$ 29. $\dfrac{(x-3)^2}{7} - \dfrac{(y-2)^2}{9} = 1.$

37. Ellipse.   39. Hyperbola.   41. Hyperbola.   43. Parabola.

45. $x = -y - 1$, $x = 2y$. Hence the graph is two intersecting lines.

49. The greatest value is $\frac{11}{2}$.

EXERCISE 6–1

1. 0.   3. -5.   5. $4x^3$.   7. 2.

9. $3x^2$.   11. $6x - 4$.   13. $-3x^{-4}$.   15. $-1/x^2$.

17. $-12x^{-5} + 10x^{-3}$.   19. $-4/x^5$.

21. $D_x y = 2x$; $2x - y = 1$.   23. $D_x y = -1/x^2$; $x + y + 2 = 0$.

25. $D_x y = 2x - 4$; $y = -4$.   27. $D_x y = 4x^3 - 8x$; $16x - y = 32$.

29. $D_x y = -4x^{-5} + 4x^3$; $y = 2$.

EXERCISE 6–2

1. $(0,2)$, maximum point. The slope is positive when $x < 0$ and negative when $x > 0$.

3. $(2,-4)$ minimum point. The slope is negative when $x < 2$ and positive when $x > 2$.

5. $(3,10)$, maximum point. The slope is positive when $x < 3$ and negative when $x > 3$.

7. $(0,0)$, neither a maximum nor a minimum point. The slope is negative at all points except the origin.

9. The slope is zero at $(1,\frac{1}{3})$ and is positive at all other points.

11. $(-1,1)$, maximum point; $(0,0)$, minimum point. The slope is positive when $x < -1$ and when $x > 0$. The slope is negative when $-1 < x < 0$.

13. $(0,4)$, maximum point; $(2,0)$, minimum point. The slope is positive when $x < 0$ and when $x > 2$. The slope is negative when $0 < x < 2$.

15. $(0,0)$, $(1,-1)$.   17. $(0,1)$, $(1,\frac{13}{12})$.

19. $(0,1)$, $(1,\frac{5}{4})$, $(2,1)$.   21. $(-1,\frac{5}{12})$, $(1,-\frac{11}{12})$.

EXERCISE 6–3

1. A square 100 yds. on a side.   3. 2000 sq. yd.

5. $\dfrac{10 - 2\sqrt{7}}{3} = 1.57$ in., approximately.   7. $6'$ by $6'$ by $3'$.

9. Radius 2 in., height 4 in.   11. $\dfrac{250{,}000}{27}$ cu. in.

EXERCISE 7–1

1. Period $\frac{2}{3}\pi$, amplitude 1.   3. Period 6π, amplitude 1.

5. Period $\frac{1}{5}\pi$.   7. Period $\frac{1}{3}\pi$.   9. Period $\frac{4}{3}\pi$.   11. Period 4, amplitude 2.

Exercise 8–1

1. $(x - 2)^2 + (y + 3)^2 = 25$.
3. $y^2 - 6x - 4y + 13 = 0$.
5. $x^2 + y^2 = 25$.
7. $x^2 + y^2 - 8x + 2y + 9 = 0$.
9. $y^2 - 2y + 16x + 65 = 0$.
11. $3x^2 - y^2 + 10x - 25 = 0$.
13. $9x^2 - 16y^2 = 144$.

15. Equation of path: $(1 - e^2)x^2 + y^2 - 2kx + k^2 = 0$. When $0 < e < 1$, the coefficients of x^2 and y^2 are of like sign and unequal and the path is an ellipse. When $e > 1$, the coefficients of x^2 and y^2 are of unlike signs and the path is a hyperbola. When $e = 1$, the equation becomes $y^2 = 2k(x - \frac{1}{2}k)$ and the path is a parabola. When $y = 0$, we have $(1 - e^2)x^2 - 2kx + k^2 = 0$, and $x = k/(1 + e)$, $k/(1 - e)$. Hence the vertices are at $(k/1 + e,0)$ and $(k/1 - e,0)$. The center, midway between the vertices, is $(k/1 - e^2,0)$.

17. $x^2 + y^2 - 5x - y = 0$.
19. $y = 2x^2 - 3x$.

Exercise 8–2

We assume that the data in the remaining problems of Chapter 8 justify the retention of three significant figures in the answers.

1. $y = -0.718x + 8.71$.
3. $y = 0.100x + 10.0$.
5. $N = 1380t + 6300$.

Exercise 8–3

1. $y = 0.121x^{3.13}$.
3. $t = 0.259s^{0.488}$.
5. $p = 103v^{-1.39}$.

Exercise 8–4

1. $y = 2.00 \cdot 10^{0.131x}$
3. $y = 9.91 \log x + 3.03$.
5. $T = 99.5 \cdot 10^{-0.0989t}$
7. $V = 3.87 \log P - 0.828$.

Exercise 9–1

1. Other coordinates of $(3,60°)$: $(-3,240°)$, $(-3,-120°)$, $(3,-300°)$. Other coordinates of $(6,-30°)$: $(6,330°)$, $(-6,150°)$, $(-6,-210°)$. Other coordinates of $(2,180°)$: $(-2,0°)$, $(2,-180°)$, $(-2,360°)$. Other coordinates of $(-3,-225°)$: $(3,-45°)$, $(3,315°)$, $(-3,135°)$. The point $(0,10°)$ is the pole. The pole may be represented by $(0,\theta)$, where θ is any angle.

3. (a) and (b) On a circle of radius 4 and center at the pole; (c) on a line through the origin with an inclination of 45°; (d) on a vertical line through the origin.

Exercise 9–2

1. $(0,4)$.
3. $(7,0)$.
5. $(0,8)$.
7. $(-3\sqrt{3},3)$.
9. $(-9,0)$.
11. $(3,0°)$.
13. $(1,180°)$.
15. $(2,45°)$.
17. $(4,150°)$.
19. $(5,143°)$, nearest degree.
21. $(13,247°)$.
23. $\rho \sin \theta = -4$.
25. $\tan \theta = -3$.
27. $\rho = \dfrac{D}{A \cos \theta + B \sin \theta}$.
29. $\rho^2 \sin \theta \cos \theta = a^2$.
31. $\rho^2 \cos 2\theta = a^2$.
33. $\rho^2 = a^2 \sin 2\theta$.
35. $y = 0$.
37. $x^2 + y^2 - 2x - 2y = 0$.
39. $x^2 + y^2 - 8x = 0$.
41. $x = 6$.
43. $x^2 - y^2 = a^2$.
45. $y^2 + 6x - 9 = 0$.
47. $3x^2 - y^2 + 8x + 4 = 0$.
49. $x - 2y + 5 = 0$.

EXERCISE 9–4

7. Center $(4,0°)$, radius 4.   9. Center $(5,270°)$, radius 5.
11. (a) $\rho^2 - 8\rho \cos \theta + 12 = 0$;   (b) $\rho^2 - 8\rho \sin \theta + 12 = 0$;
(c) $\rho - 4 \cos \theta = 0$.

EXERCISE 9–6

1. $(1,60°)$, $(1,300°)$.   3. $(3\sqrt{2},45°)$, $(3\sqrt{2},315°)$.
5. $(a,90°)$, $(a,270°)$.   7. $(2,0°)$.   9. $(\frac{4}{3},60°)$, $(\frac{4}{3},300°)$.
11. $(1,0°)$, $(-\frac{3}{5},233°)$.   Arc sin $(-\frac{4}{5}) = 233°$, to the nearest degree.
13. $(1,60°)$.   15. $(1,60°)$, $(1,300°)$.
17. $(3,180°)$.   19. $(2,60°)$, $(2,300°)$, $(-1,180°)$.

EXERCISE 10–1

1. $3x + y = 6$.   3. $xy = 6$.   5. $x^2 + 9y = 9$,
7. $9x^2 + 16y^2 = 144$.   9. $x^2 + y^2 = 2x$.   11. $x^2 + 4y = 4$.
13. $x^2 - y^2 = 1$.   15. $x^2 + xy - 1 = 0$.
17. $2x^2 - 2xy + y^2 = 1$.   19. $y^2 - x^2 = 4$.

EXERCISE 10–2

1. $x = 40\sqrt{2}t$, $y = 40\sqrt{2}t - 16t^2$; $x^2 - 200x + 200y = 0$.   The greatest height is 50 feet, and the ball strikes the ground 100 feet away.

3. $x = v_0t$, $y = -\frac{1}{2}gt^2$; $y = -\dfrac{gx^2}{2v_0^2}$.   In 2 seconds the projectile falls 60 feet and travels $2v_0$ feet horizontally.

EXERCISE 12–1

1. $-2\mathbf{i} + 8\mathbf{j}, 6\mathbf{i} - 2\mathbf{j}$.   3. $2\mathbf{i} - 6\mathbf{j}, 4\mathbf{i} + 2\mathbf{j}$.
5. $\dfrac{3\mathbf{i} + 4\mathbf{j}}{5}$.   7. $\dfrac{12\mathbf{i} - 5\mathbf{j}}{13}$.   9. $\dfrac{\mathbf{i} + 2\mathbf{j}}{\sqrt{5}}$.   11. $\sqrt{2}, \dfrac{1}{\sqrt{2}}$.

13 $1,1$.   15. $\sqrt{13}, -\dfrac{3}{\sqrt{13}}$.   17. $4\mathbf{i} - \mathbf{j}$.

EXEECISE 12–2

1. 11.   3. $\sqrt{102}$.

5. $\overrightarrow{AB} = -6\mathbf{i} - 6\mathbf{j}$, $\overrightarrow{BC} = -6\mathbf{j} - 6\mathbf{k}$, $\overrightarrow{CA} = 6\mathbf{i} + 12\mathbf{j} + 6\mathbf{k}$.   The lengths are $6\sqrt{2}, 6\sqrt{2}, 6\sqrt{6}$.

7. $\overrightarrow{AB} = \mathbf{i} + 2\mathbf{j} + 2\mathbf{k}$, $\overrightarrow{BC} = -3\mathbf{i} - 3\mathbf{j}$, $\overrightarrow{CA} = 2\mathbf{i} + \mathbf{j} - 2\mathbf{k}$.   The lengths are $3, 3\sqrt{2}, 3$.

9. $\dfrac{6\mathbf{i} + 3\mathbf{j} - 6\mathbf{k}}{9}$.   11. $\dfrac{2\mathbf{i} - \mathbf{j} - 3\mathbf{k}}{\sqrt{14}}$.

13. $4\mathbf{i} + \frac{5}{2}\mathbf{j}$, to the mid-point; $3\mathbf{i} - \mathbf{j} + 4\mathbf{k}$ and $5\mathbf{i} + \mathbf{j} + \mathbf{k}$, to the trisection points.

15. Center $(-2,1,-3)$, radius $\sqrt{14}$.   17. $\mathbf{i} + 2\mathbf{j} + 2\mathbf{k}$.

EXERCISE 12-3

1. $-2, -\frac{2}{27}$.

3. $13, \frac{13}{105}$.

5. $\frac{19}{3}\sqrt{3}, \frac{19}{3}(i - j - k)$.

7. $55°$.

9. $64°, 90°, 26°$.

EXERCISE 12-4

1. $3x - 2y + 5z - 11 = 0$.

3. $2x - 3y - 4z = 8$.

5. $3x + 9y - 4z = 0$.

7. $2x + 3y - 4z - 2 = 0$.

9. $\frac{8}{3}$.

11. $\frac{2}{7}\sqrt{21}$.

13 $\frac{1}{6}\sqrt{6}$.

15. 0.

EXERCISE 12-5

1. $2i + j + 3k$; $(0,-5,-12)$, $(10,0,3)$, $(8,-1,0)$.

3. $3i - j + 2k$; $(0,1,2)$, $(3,0,4)$, $(-3,2,0)$.

5. $\dfrac{x - 4}{-2} = \dfrac{y + 3}{3} = \dfrac{z - 5}{4}$; $x = 4 - 2t, y = -3 + 3t, z = 5 + 4t$.

7. $\dfrac{x - 1}{2} = \dfrac{y - 1}{3} = \dfrac{z - 2}{-1}$; $x = 1 + 2t, y = 1 + 3t, z = 2 - t$.

9. $\dfrac{x - 2}{2} = \dfrac{y + 1}{1}$, $z - 1 = 0$; $x = 2 + 2t, y = -1 + t, z = 1$.

11. $\dfrac{y - 3}{1} = \dfrac{z - 2}{2}$, $x - 4 = 0$; $x = 4, y = 3 + t, z = 2 + 2t$.

13. $x = 0, z = 0$; $x = 0, y = t, z = 0$.

15. $\dfrac{x - 1}{3} = \dfrac{y - 2}{-2} = \dfrac{z - 3}{3}$.

17. $\dfrac{x - 1}{1} = \dfrac{y}{-2} = \dfrac{z - 2}{1}$.

19. $\dfrac{y - 5}{1} = \dfrac{z - 4}{1}$, $x = 2$.

21. $y - 3 = 0, z - 4 = 0$.

23. $\dfrac{x - 2}{3} = \dfrac{y - 3}{-1} = \dfrac{z}{2}$.

25. $\dfrac{x}{2} = \dfrac{y - 3}{-3} = \dfrac{z - 6}{1}$.

27. $\dfrac{2}{\sqrt{14}}, \dfrac{1}{\sqrt{14}}, \dfrac{3}{\sqrt{14}}; \dfrac{-2}{\sqrt{6}}, \dfrac{1}{\sqrt{6}}, \dfrac{1}{\sqrt{6}}; \dfrac{3}{\sqrt{14}}, \dfrac{-1}{\sqrt{14}}, \dfrac{2}{\sqrt{14}}; \dfrac{1}{\sqrt{14}}, \dfrac{2}{\sqrt{14}}, \dfrac{3}{\sqrt{14}}$.

29. $\dfrac{11}{21}$.

31. $\dfrac{2}{7}$.

33. $\dfrac{x - 2}{2} = \dfrac{y - 1}{10} = \dfrac{z - 3}{13}$.

INDEX